Emotional Fitness
Developing a Wholesome Heart

David Ferguson
Don McMinn

Copyright, 2003

Emotional Fitness

David Ferguson and Don McMinn

First edition—2003
6Acts Ministry under license agreement from Intimacy Press
2322 Creekside Circle South, Irving, Texas, 75063
972.432.8690
dmcminn@6Acts.org

Printed in the United States for Worldwide Distribution
ISBN—0-9703229-5-X

Emotional Fitness

Table of Contents

How to get the most out of this workbook

1. Don't process this workbook alone - work through the book with a journeymate. A journeymate is someone

- *Who cares for you.* You're not going to share your deepest feelings with someone unless you're convinced that he cares for you. You must sense that he cares for you just because of who you are, not because of what you do or how well you perform.
- *Whom you can trust.* You'll also be reluctant to vulnerably share your life with someone unless you know you can trust him. A trustworthy journeymate must be confidential about any sensitive information you may share, respond with compassion and acceptance to your hurts, not use any information shared in confidence against you, and not allow any information to adversely affect your relationship.
- *Who is available.* You may have a friend who cares about you and is trustworthy, but if he's not available when you need him, you'll still be alone. This is one of those times when availability is more important than ability.

    If you're married, we encourage you to work through this book with your spouse, even if the relationship doesn't have all the ingredients of an ideal journeymate. Hopefully, this workbook will help establish that level of trust and oneness. If you're single, ask a close friend or relative to be your journeymate.

2. Complete all the personal assessment questions in each chapter even if they seem trivial, obvious, or oblique. (These are the fill-in-the blank sections within the body of each chapter.) They are specifically designed to help you process some critical issues.

How to structure the course

There are eleven chapters so it will take at least eleven weeks to finish this workbook. Each chapter includes a discussion of a particular topic, personal assessment questions, discussion questions, journeymate questions, and a homework assignment.

Prior to each session each participant should read the next chapter and respond to the specific questions when prompted.

This workbook can be processed in several different ways.

1. You and your journeymate meet weekly to discuss the content of the current lesson, process the discussion questions, and process the journeymate section. [Allow 60-90 minutes.]

2. You and your journeymate meet weekly with 2-5 other couples to discuss the content of the current lesson and process the discussion questions in the group. Also, depending on the level of trust and vulnerability in the group, the journeymate questions can be discussed in the large group or just among journeymates. [Allow 60-90 minutes.]

3. You and your journeymate can be part of a large class. If you use the class approach, don't resort to the "talking head" approach to teaching (one master teacher talking to the class with no class interaction). If a master teacher is used, the class can be divided into smaller groups for group discussion. [Allow 90+ minutes.]

If using the Facilitator's Guide, it is not necessary for students to read Chapter 1 prior to the first meeting. But prior to subsequent sessions, each participant should read the next chapter and complete the fill-in-the-blank sections.

The Facilitator's Guide includes learning activities that further illustrate the principles being discussed. Depending on available time, interest and resources, these activities can be acted out as drama skits or they can simply be read aloud. We encourage you to include these as a part of your group time because they enhance the understanding of the principles and help put them in a real life setting.

Dealing with Your Feelings

It is with the heart that one sees rightly; what is essential is invisible to the eye.
Antoine De Saint-Exupery

In this workbook, we'll be talking a lot about emotions. Before we begin, we'd like to find out what *you* think about human emotionality and how you would assess your own emotional condition. So take a few minutes to comment on the following issues.

Your thoughts on human emotionality:

1. True or False - *Deal with your emotions or your emotions will deal with you.*
   [Circle your answer and write out a brief explanation.]

_____

_____

_____

2. Respond to this statement: *Emotions that are "buried" are "buried alive."*

_____

_____

_____

3. How important is emotional closeness to the development of intimate relationships?
   [Place an "x" on the line.]

_____

Very important   **Moderately important**   **Unimportant**

Explain your response:

_____

_____

_____

4. How important is emotional health to a person's overall well-being? [Place an "x" on the line.]

Very important	Moderately important	Unimportant

Explain your response:

_____

_____

5. Are *correct, logical thinking* and *emotional health* mutually exclusive? Can a person be *fully emotional* and *cognitively sharp* at the same time? Explain your answer:

_____

_____

_____

Exploring the status of your personal emotional life:

1. Write down as many human emotions as you can. (Ex. *I feel...happy, embarrassed*, etc.)

_____

_____

_____

2. What emotions do you struggle with the most?

_____

_____

3. How emotionally expressive are you? [Put an "x" on the line.]

Very emotional	-	Moderately emotional	-	Somewhat unemotional	-	"Like a rock"/stoic

Why is *Emotional Fitness* so important?

1. Emotional Fitness will help you live a balanced and meaningful life.

It's been said, "Deal with your emotions or your emotions will deal with you." That's good advice. When God created mankind he placed emotions in our DNA, therefore we need to learn how to deal with them. Often, people suffer from one of two emotional extremes: some are out of control emotionally; their emotions keep them on a constant roller coaster ride and they live in a constant state of turmoil. Their emotions rule their lives. The other extreme includes people who deny their emotionality; they think the key to emotional health is to be non-emotional. Both extremes are unhealthy. Balance is the key. In this workbook, you'll discover the path to emotional health – to become emotionally self-aware and to learn how to manage your emotions.

Emotional health is perhaps the main determining factor in whether or not you are happy in life. Factual knowledge itself, while important, is not sufficient. You can know exactly what E=mc² means and still be miserable if you are filled with fear, anger, hurt, or condemnation. Even physical health is not as significant as emotional health in determining true happiness. A person can be struggling physically and still enjoy inward peace and happiness.

2. Understanding human emotionality will allow us to properly respond to other peoples' emotions.

It's also been said, "Learn to deal with *other people's* emotions, or their emotions will deal with you." We must learn not only to manage our *own* emotions, but also to respond correctly to others' emotions. For instance, we must learn how to deal with our own anger, but we also need to know how to deal with anger in others. What *do* you do when a co-worker gets angry and begins to yell at you?

For better or for worse, we *are* affected by the emotionality of those close to us. If we don't understand other people's emotions and don't know how to properly respond to them, we may end up being emotionally abused. Also, if we don't learn how to properly respond to the emotions of others when they feel hurt, angry, or fearful, we will lack the skills to genuinely care for them and help them negotiate their own emotions.

3. Understanding human emotionality is a fundamental "people skill," and having good people skills is a critical part of being successful in life.

Let's face it – we're surrounded by six billion people – and we interact with a few or many of them every day. Depending on our profession, each of us needs to learn a specific skill set (accounting, mechanical, musical, educational), but *all of us* need to learn and master people skills. If we don't learn how to get along with others, we'll live frustrating, ineffective lives.

Even from a practical, financial perspective, learning how to get along with others is a necessary life skill. Lee Iacocca once said, "The kiss of death on anyone's personnel file is that they don't know how to get along with people." Perhaps the most important skill a business person can learn is how to relate to other people – and a fundamental aspect of that is learning to relate to others on an emotional level.

{ The human personality is said to consist of roughly four-fifths emotions and one-fifth intellect. This means that our decisions are made on the basis of 80% emotions and only 20% intellect. To engage in a confrontation or even a discussion without taking emotions into account is to be only 20% effective in your dealings with people.

4. Understanding human emotionality is a prerequisite for developing close, intimate relationships.

It is difficult, if not impossible, to be truly close to another person without engaging emotionally. Two people may *think* the same way (share the same political, theological, social convictions), enjoy the same activities (hobbies, interests), work toward common goals, and even spend a lot of time together, but the relationship will remain superficial and shallow if emotions are ignored or neglected. A critical factor in developing intimacy in a relationship is that we must share all of ourselves, including our emotions. Can you envision the shallowness of a relationship in which emotions are never shared?

On the other hand, when we *do* emotionally engage with another person, it's amazing how fast a relationship can become deep and meaningful. In our training programs, we often have three or four people meet together as a group for several hours a day over a three-day period, and we encourage them to be open and vulnerable with each other. At the end of their time together, it's not uncommon for people to say, "I feel closer to the members of my group, after only three days of being together, than I feel toward other people that I have known all of my life." The difference? In the small groups they shared on an emotional level.

When we teach marriage seminars, in one of the sessions we talk about the three dimensions of oneness in marriage. Every husband and wife should strive to become one spiritually, physically, and emotionally. All three areas are important, but often, the emotional area is the most neglected. Even though a couple may enjoy spiritual and physical closeness, the marriage will suffer if they are emotionally removed from each other.

5. Only by engaging with others on an emotional level will our aloneness be removed.

In Genesis 2:18, God made a statement that defines the very nature of man; "It is not good for man to be alone."

Aloneness is primarily an issue of the human heart - an emotional issue. It's certainly not just a physical issue, because I can be in the same room with 100 other people and still feel alone. Neither is it a mental issue, because though I may have the same beliefs and convictions as others, I can still feel relationally distant. Aloneness is an issue of the heart that can be removed only through intimate relationships, and relationships cannot be intimate without the emotional dimension.

Emotionality and Christianity

Human emotionality has often been minimized, if not criticized, by the Christian community. Some people have so exalted the virtues of proper thinking (embracing truth) that emotions are viewed as unimportant, optional, and even undesirable. But the alleged conflict between fact and feeling is not an issue with God. As surely as God created us with a mind, he gave us emotions. We don't have to choose between one and the other - they are not mutually exclusive.

The appropriateness of emotions is forever settled by realizing that God himself is emotional. Notice the emotionality of God in Genesis 6:6; "The Lord was **grieved** that he had made man on the earth, and his heart was **filled with pain**."

Human emotionality is further confirmed in the fact that Jesus and the Holy Spirit feel and express emotions. In Mark 3:5, the Pharisees were looking for a reason to accuse Jesus, so they watched him closely to see if he would heal on the Sabbath. When Jesus saw them, two different emotions surged through his heart: "Jesus looked around at them in **anger**, **deeply distressed** at their stubborn hearts." In Luke 10:21, the Scriptures record that "Jesus, **full of joy** through the Holy Spirit, said..." Paul taught that the Holy Spirit can feel **grieved** (Ephesians 4:30).

If God is emotional and expresses emotions, it must be okay for us to be and do likewise. We are created in God's image, and we are to emulate him.

As you consider your spiritual background, what message did you receive relative to emotions?

If emotions are so important, why do some people seem to be "emotional rocks"?

Although we were created as emotional beings, it is possible to become emotionally cold and unfeeling.

When someone is emotionally "unplugged," it's important to realize that God did not create him that way. When the adult "emotional rock" was a newborn, he did not hesitate to cry when he was upset or squeal when he was happy. How then, do emotions become suppressed?

Part of the answer lies in our society's concept of proper emotional expression, particularly relative to emotional "gender bias." For instance, young boys are often taught that "big boys don't cry," so if a six-year-old boy falls on the playground and scrapes his knee, he'll be told to "Suck it up and go on." But if a six-year-old girl experiences similar pain, she may be held and comforted. Often, emotional expression is discouraged in males but encouraged in females. In recent years, in the quest for gender equality, cultural pressure has often encouraged women to minimize their emotionality. In truth, all children, whether male or female, are created with a similar range of emotional capacity, and their emotionality should be equally encouraged and developed.

Unhealed hurt and pain is another cause of emotional numbness. A person's emotions can be so damaged by unhealed hurt and pain that he or she "turns off the emotions" to avoid more pain. A person with this level of unresolved pain may subconsciously think, "Every time I get in touch with my emotions, I hurt. I don't want to hurt anymore, so I'll simply 'turn off' my emotions." Or, "I don't want to hurt alone (without someone's comforting care), so I will simply not allow myself to be hurt; I'll become emotionally indifferent."

> Psychiatrists have a term for someone who is emotionally blank – *alexithymia*, from the Greek *a*-for "lack," *lexis* for "word," and *thymos* for "emotion."

But when we disengage emotionally, we're not able to experience life as God intended it. We will also have difficulty understanding other people's emotions and may become intolerant of their normal, healthy emotional needs. The truth is, we cannot really "turn off" our emotions, so we end up ignoring and "stuffing" them and even the emotions of those around us.

Emotions are natural and essential. To experience the abundant life that Christ promised, we must be emotionally alive and healthy.

For emotions to remain healthy, we must learn how to manage them properly and also learn how to relate emotionally to other people. The key to both is to learn the biblical principles of **Emotional Expression** and **Emotional Responding**.

Emotional Expression

Emotions should be truthfully and properly expressed. God never intended for us to deny or suppress our feelings. Proper emotional expression depends on several factors:

1. We must be open and honest with God and others.

We should be honest and vulnerable with God about our joys, anxieties, fears, and hurts. Our emotions are not a surprise to God, so why not share with him how we are feeling?

We also need to share our emotions with other people. We all need friends with whom we can share our emotions, people with whom we can be open, transparent, and vulnerable and who will care about how we feel and respond appropriately. If you're married, ideally this will include your spouse. If you have children, this is one of the most important roles a parent can play. If you're single, you need close friends with whom you can share your deepest feelings.

2. We need to develop an "emotional vocabulary."

Earlier when we asked you to list all the emotions you could think of, how many did you write down? Most people can think only of 10-15 emotions, and this lack of an emotional vocabulary restricts our ability to articulate how we're feeling. When asked, "How are you feeling?" we often reply, "I don't know" because we're not equipped to identify our feelings.

Over 300 human emotions have been identified. Here are just a few:

Giving names to emotions

Emotions . . . How Do You Feel?

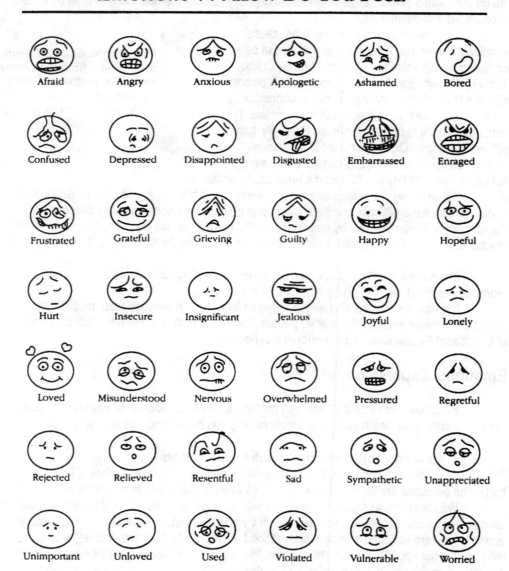

Afraid	Angry	Anxious	Apologetic	Ashamed	Bored
Confused	Depressed	Disappointed	Disgusted	Embarrassed	Enraged
Frustrated	Grateful	Grieving	Guilty	Happy	Hopeful
Hurt	Insecure	Insignificant	Jealous	Joyful	Lonely
Loved	Misunderstood	Nervous	Overwhelmed	Pressured	Regretful
Rejected	Relieved	Resentful	Sad	Sympathetic	Unappreciated
Unimportant	Unloved	Used	Violated	Vulnerable	Worried

Identifying Emotions

Listed below are 13 emotions and 13 scenarios that could have caused each of the emotions. Match and fill in the emotion with the scenario.

Comforted, belittled, used, supported, ignored, alone, sad, respected, secure, disrespected, embarrassed, happy, accepted.

➢ *Today when I left the office, it was raining. When I reached the sidewalk, I slipped and fell right in front of everyone. I felt _____.*

➢ *I went to lunch with three old friends from high school that I haven't seen in years. Not once in the conversation did anyone ask about me. I felt _____.*

➢ *I was so upset at work today. But when I came home my husband listened to me, spoke caring words and then held me. I felt _____.*

➢ *This is my first week of college. I'm 500 miles from home and don't know a soul. I feel _____.*

➢ *I was the only person in my math class who couldn't work a particular algebra problem. My teacher made me go to the board and try to figure it out. He knew I couldn't do it, but he didn't offer any help. I felt _____.*

➢ *In our staff meeting today, my boss asked for everyone's opinion but mine. I felt _____.*

➢ *When I was growing up, I knew my mom and dad loved each other and were committed to each other for life. I felt _____.*

➢ *I worked for days on the school auction. I never heard a "good job" or even a "we appreciate you." I feel _____.*

➢ *Last semester I felt incapable of passing a course I was taking at college. My friend volunteered to tutor me and with her help, I passed! I felt _____.*

➢ *My parents always encouraged me to be myself; I never felt pressured to try to be like anyone else. I felt _____.*

➢ *My mother passed away a year ago today. I really miss her. I feel _____.*

➢ *Right in the middle of staff meeting, my boss asked my opinion about one of our important clients. I felt _____.*

➢ *I worked hard to get a part in the school play. I found out today I got the lead role. I felt _____.*

During any 24-hour period, we experience a wide range of emotions. A psychologist who was studying human emotionality placed a pager on ten volunteers. He beeped them at various times during the day and when paged, they were to write down the emotions they were feeling at that moment. He was trying to increase their awareness of their emotional condition and their ability to identify their emotions. Not a bad exercise.

3. Once we develop an emotional vocabulary, we need to use it.

We need to become comfortable with *sharing* our emotions - not just cognitively *identifying* our emotions, but actually using words and phrases to express how we're feeling. For instance, consider how you *feel* when someone says something hurtful to you. Express what you're *feeling*; don't just logically analyze what happened and report the facts (For example: "This person just said something hurtful to me; I must be hurt."); use words to express your feelings.

Emotional Responding

When someone expresses emotion, the only proper initial response is to respond emotionally. Emotional expression demands an emotional response, but we are often tempted to offer ineffective substitutes:

> Someone emotionally shares - "I was disappointed and hurt that we didn't get to go on the outing we had planned."
> And in return, he or she may receive
> - **Logic or reasoning** – "Obviously, I wouldn't have made plans for a date if I'd known this business trip was going to come up." Or, "I couldn't have gone anyway with this sore throat. That's just the way things worked out."
> - **Criticism** – "You surely are being sensitive about this. I didn't think this date was going to be such a big deal!"
> - **Complaints** – "Well, I'm hurt too. We could have spent last weekend together, but you went to your sister's instead."
> - **Neglect** – "Can't we just drop it! I really don't want to discuss this."

These responses always miss the mark, leaving the receiver empty, hurt, and alone. An appropriate emotional response in this situation would include an empathetic statement such as "I realize that you're hurt and disappointed; you have every right to feel that way. I really regret we didn't get to go out as planned. I know you were looking forward to the time together, and so was I."

There's nothing *wrong* with a logical response, it's just not the best *initial* response. Often, when someone is emotionally upset, it's difficult for him to respond to logic or reasoning. But once his emotions have been acknowledged and properly addressed, he is then able to deal with the situation on a cognitive level.

Head to Head: Heart to Heart

Whenever we talk, we can speak from our *head* (logic, reasoning, facts) or from our *heart* (feelings, emotions).

When someone speaks from his head, it's appropriate to respond with a head response.

       Dwayne – "It sure is hot outside." [A head statement.]

       Chris – "Yes, it is hot, and it's going to be even hotter tomorrow." [A head statement.]

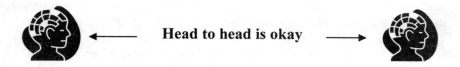

Head to head is okay

When someone speaks from his heart; we should respond with a heart answer.

       Dwayne – "It's so hot outside. I had a flat tire on the way home from work and I got so frustrated having to change the tire out in the heat." [A heart statement.]

       Chris – "I'm sorry you got frustrated. I can imagine how annoying it must have been to have to change the tire, particularly in this heat." [An appropriate heart answer.]

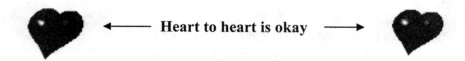

Heart to heart is okay

When someone speaks from his head and we respond with a heart response, it may seem inappropriate.

       Dwayne – "It sure is hot outside." [A head statement.]

       Chris – "Oh, I'm so sorry; are you all right?" [An inappropriate heart response.]

When someone speaks from his heart and we respond with a head response, it can seem uncaring and callous.

       Dwayne – "It's so hot outside. I had a flat tire on the way home from work and I got so frustrated having to change the tire out in the heat." [A heart statement.]

       Chris – "Yes, it is hot, and it's going to be even hotter tomorrow." [An inappropriate head statement.]

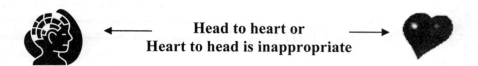

**Head to heart or
Heart to head is inappropriate**

Write about a time in the past few days when someone spoke from her heart. She wasn't necessarily trying to communicate facts or statistics; she was expressing emotions.

_____

_____

How did you respond?

_____

_____

9

Discussion questions (Discuss these issues in your group or with your journeymate.)

1. What was the most interesting concept in this chapter?
2. Why has the Christian community seemed reluctant to embrace human emotionality?
3. Share with the group your responses to the *Exploring the status of your personal emotional life* section (page 2).
4. How do the following Scriptures relate to emotional expression/responding?
   - "A word aptly spoken is like apples of gold in settings of silver" (Proverbs 25:11).
   - "Do not let any unwholesome talk come out of your mouths, but only what is helpful for building others up according to their needs, that it may benefit those who listen" (Ephesians 4:29).

Journeymate time (Discuss these issues with your journeymate.)

1. Share with your journeymate your responses to the fill-in-the-blank sections in this chapter.
2. Discuss these issues:
   How adept are you at sensing other people's emotional condition?
   How adept are you at responding appropriately to other people's emotions?
   How adept are you at expressing your own emotions?

Homework (To be completed before the next meeting.)

1. In the coming week, set aside about 20 minutes each day to share with your journeymate the predominant emotions you felt during the day. Allow him or her to respond appropriately.

Keep a journal of your experiences.
Day 1 - The predominant emotions I felt today were _____
Day 2 - The predominant emotions I felt today were _____
Day 3 - The predominant emotions I felt today were _____
Day 4 - The predominant emotions I felt today were _____
Day 5 - The predominant emotions I felt today were _____
Day 6 - The predominant emotions I felt today were _____
Day 7 - The predominant emotions I felt today were _____

2. Read and process Chapter 2.

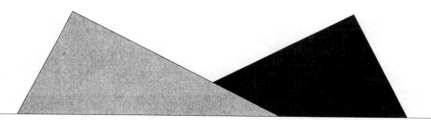

Chapter Summary

1. Emotional health is an indispensable part of living a balanced and meaningful life and is a prerequisite for developing and maintaining meaningful relationships.

2. We must learn to manage our own emotions and to respond properly to other people's emotions.

3. God created us with emotions; God himself is emotional; therefore it's okay for us to feel and express emotions.

4. Emotional Expression – Emotions should be truthfully and properly expressed. God never intended for us to suppress how we feel.

5. Emotional Responding – When someone expresses emotions, the only proper, initial response is to respond emotionally.

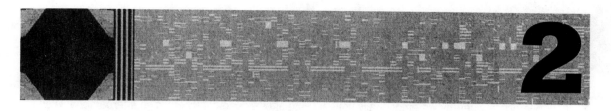

Empathy Matters

> "It was in those who had recovered from the plague that the sick and the dying found most compassion."
>
> *The historian Thucydides, 430 B.C.*

In the first chapter we discussed the fact that emotions must be expressed (Emotional Expression) and that when they are, the only proper response is an emotional one (Emotional Responding).

Now, let's go one step further.

When someone expresses emotion, we not only need to respond emotionally, but it's important to respond with a *particular type of emotion*. In other words, we can't randomly select an emotion for our response – it needs to be the right one.

First, let's talk about empathy.

Empathy

A critical requirement for proper emotional responding is the development of empathy. Empathy (Gr. *empatheia* "feeling into") is the ability to discern emotions in others and then to experience, within ourselves, the same emotion. It goes beyond sympathy, which is simply the mental awareness of the general plight of another person but with no sacrificial sharing in what is being felt.

For instance, have you ever cried with a friend, not necessarily because you were upset about what she was troubled about, but because you are sad that she is sad? Perhaps your friend just found out that her pet has died and she begins to cry, and suddenly you are crying--not because you are sad at the death of her pet (perhaps you didn't even know she had a pet), but you are crying because your friend is crying. That's empathy.

To develop empathy we must learn to listen and observe: words, sounds, and body language. Although people may not be adept at articulating how they are feeling, we can usually identify their feelings by listening with our ears, eyes, and heart. Christ's ministry is often characterized by his being "moved with compassion" as he discerned the needs and pain of others (Matthew 9:36, 20:34).

Have you ever cried *with* another person? Were you sad because of what happened to make the person cry (perhaps you both lost a mutual friend), or were you weeping simply because he was weeping? Write about your experience.

_____

_____

_____

Emotional Attunement

Empathy is synonymous with what some social scientists call *attunement*. In 1987, Daniel Stern, a psychiatrist at Cornell University, coined the word attunement to describe the process whereby we emotionally connect with another person. [Stern, *The Interpersonal World of the Infant*, Basic Books, 1987, p.30] His work focused on the emotional development of children. He noticed that when a baby squeals in delight, it's important for a parent to respond to this emotional expression by gently touching the baby, cooing, or matching the baby's pitch. This gives the baby a reassuring sense of being emotionally connected, that his emotions are okay, and that someone understands him. Attunement also happens if, when a child falls down and cries, the parent responds with sadness and gives the child a comforting hug.

> "Empathy is the fundamental 'people skill.' People who are empathetic are more attuned to the subtle social signals that indicate what others need or want."
> Daniel Goleman, *Emotional Intelligence*

Attunement does *not* occur when a child expresses a particular type of emotion (positive or painful) but receives an emotional response that is the opposite of what he's feeling. For example, if a child paints a picture and expresses delight and happiness but a parent responds with anger and frustration because he colored on the table, the child receives a contradictory signal. Likewise, if a child cries but his parents respond nonchalantly, the child may be emotionally confused. The appropriate response would be to rejoice with the child in his joy and to mourn with him in his sadness.

There are three important advantages of attunement:
1. I feel that someone cares for me and is willing to enter into my emotional world.
2. I feel that someone understands me.
3. I feel that it's okay to be emotional and express emotions; my emotions are legitimate.

Likewise, there are three corollary disadvantages of disattunement:
1. I feel that no one cares for me; I'm emotionally alone.
2. I feel that no one understands me.
3. Eventually, I'll be reluctant to express my emotions and may even begin to doubt the legitimacy of my emotions.

Romans 12:15 - Biblical Attunement

Interestingly, two thousand years ago, the Apostle Paul declared the same truth about emotional connectedness that social scientists have recently called attunement. In Romans 12:15 Paul said, "Rejoice with those who rejoice and mourn with those who mourn." How are we to respond to people's emotional expression? If they express positive emotions, we should rejoice with them; if they express painful emotions, we should mourn with them. It's a simple but powerful truth.

Two Categories of Emotions

Let's explore the possibility that all emotions can be placed in one of two categories: potentially positive and potentially painful. There are hundreds of emotions and perhaps thousands of various shades and combinations of emotions, but they all express either positive or painful feelings. For instance, place the following emotions in one of two boxes. (Circle each emotion and draw a line to the box where it fits.)

lonely
happy
apprehensive
hurt
relieved
satisfied
humiliated
refreshed
confused
encouraged
affirmed
irritable
afraid
grieved
disappointed
amused
deceived
loved

Positive Emotions

Painful Emotions

The fact that all human emotions can be placed in only two categories is very significant. Remember that in the last chapter we said there are over 300 different emotions and whenever someone expresses an emotion we must respond with the right emotion. Perhaps you did the math and wondered, "If there are 300+ emotions that can be expressed, am I going to have to learn 300+ different responses?"

Fortunately, no. We only need to learn two basic responses because all 300+ emotions can be placed in one of two categories: potentially positive and potentially painful. If we can learn how to respond to these two general emotional states, we'll be equipped to respond properly to any person.

The miracle of emotional attunement is that regardless of whether we're feeling good or bad, if someone enters into our emotional state and empathizes with us, we ultimately feel blessed!

Positive emotions expressed + rejoicing = feeling blessed.
Painful emotions expressed + mourning = feeling blessed.

Here's a case study on how emotional expression and responding can minister healing.

Life can be tough in the 7th grade, and one of the most apprehensive parts of the day is lunchtime. During classes, seating assignments are often made by the teacher, but during lunch, kids choose where they want to sit. "Who sits with whom" becomes a complicated, often senseless combination of several unrelated factors: cliques, friendships, daily popularity contests, who's absent, who's mad at whom, who's willing to share his lunch, etc.

On one particular day, Nikki takes an emotional beating. Shunned by her friends, she sits by herself. During lunchtime conversation, her friends look her way and laugh. Nikki takes it personally; she's sure they're laughing at her. She endures the remainder of the day, sits by herself on the bus ride home, and hurriedly walks to the haven of home.

The first one to meet Nikki is her mom. When her mom asks her how school went, Nikki answers, "Fine," but mom picks up on some atypical body language and actions. She notices that Nikki is brisk in her conversation, doesn't spend any time with the dog (normally a two-or-three minute exchange), and goes straight to her room and closes the door. Mom starts to pursue Nikki but is slowed down by various thoughts:

- "If Nikki's upset she can come talk to me."
- "Nikki is probably upset, but she needs to learn how to resolve problems by herself. She won't always have her mom and dad to talk things out."
- "I've had a wonderful day and I really don't want to talk about distressing issues."
- "It was probably a silly, inconsequential issue like, 'No one sat with me at lunch.'"

Her thoughts lead to a decision: "Nikki can tough it out in her room by herself."

Dad comes home several hours later, greets Mom, exchanges pleasantries and then asks about Nikki. Mom replies, "She must have had a bad day; she's been in her room since school was out."

Dad goes to Nikki's room, gently knocks on the door, and asks admittance. He gets a reluctant "Yes."

"Hi, Nikki."
"Hi, Dad."
"What's happening?"
"Just doing some homework."
"How was school?"
"It was okay."
"Okay, but not great?"
"Yeah."
"Hmm…. I can tell something hurtful happened. Want to talk about it?"
"It's no big deal."
"Well, if it hurt you, I'm interested, even if it's a 'small' deal. Please tell me what happened."
"Things really went okay until we got to lunch. I usually sit with Jodie and Jessica, but Jodie was absent, and Jessica was acting really weird. She just ignored me and sat with some other kids. I had to sit all by myself. Right before the bell rang, Jessica and the others looked at me and started

laughing. I felt so embarrassed."

[Dad reaches out and holds Nikki's hand.]

"I am so sorry. I know that was embarrassing. And I really hurt for you that you had to sit by yourself."

[Nikki begins to sob gently.]

"I often feel so awkward. A lot of times I don't know what to say around people."

"I know you must be confused and lonely at times; I'm really sad because I love you so much, and it hurts me to see you hurting."

[Dad gives Nikki a comforting embrace, and they sit quietly without speaking for a time.]

"Nikki, you're such a wonderful girl. Being a teenager can be tough--just discovering who you are can be painful. I can remember being in the 7th grade. One of my most stressful times came right after lunch."

"After lunch?"

"Yeah, that's when all the guys would divide up into teams and play baseball. And, of course, the girls would watch."

"What was so stressful about that?"

"I was always one of the last ones picked because I wasn't very good and no one wanted me on their team."

"You?"

"Yes, me. I felt embarrassed and unimportant..."

"Yeah, like your friends preferred everyone else instead of you?"

"Exactly–and it really hurt."

"I can't believe you ever felt that way."

"I felt that way quite often. Athletics was such an important issue at our school, and, quite frankly, I just wasn't a good athlete. I was good at math and science, but that didn't seem to matter much to the other kids."

"Did they ever call you names?"

"Oh, yes, back then they called us 'geeks.' Now the same people call us 'boss.'"

"Dad..."

"Nikki, you're special just the way you are. Don't worry about changing a thing about yourself. Just know that your mom and I love you."

"Thanks, Dad."

Nikki's father empathized with her. He sensed that something was wrong, took the time to enter into her world, identified with her pain, and responded appropriately to her feelings. In this case, after comforting Nikki emotionally, he was able to share a somewhat similar experience from his own life. He was vulnerable about his own pain. Dad "mourned with someone who was mourning." He and Nikki experienced Romans 12:15, and both were blessed.

That's what it means to connect emotionally with another person, to attune.

General principles on emotional expression and responding.

1. Emotional expression and responding is a life-long need.

Although emotional expression and responding is a critical, important part of a child's emotional development, it's not a childhood need that we outgrow; it's a lifelong need. When a young boy comes home crying because the neighborhood bully pushed him around, he needs someone to comfort him. Forty years later, when he comes home hurting because someone at the office pushed him around, he needs the same thing—comfort. When a young girl scores a soccer goal, she needs someone to rejoice with her. Forty years later, when she closes the big deal at work, she still needs someone with whom to rejoice. The truth of Romans 12:15 has no age limit.

2. We need to experience emotional expression and responding frequently.

We need to connect emotionally with another person frequently—daily, if possible. Since our emotions are stirred up daily, we need to emotionally "debrief" on a regular basis. It doesn't need to take a lot of time; sometimes only five minutes is sufficient. A good primer is simply to ask, "How are you feeling about your day?" As trust and vulnerability are established in relationships, we will be able to respond truthfully to that question, confident that when we share our emotions, our journeymate will respond with empathy and compassion. We'll be able to share vulnerably and hopefully receive an emotional response.

Disclosure	Response
• *I felt very satisfied today. I finished the project I was working on.*	*I'm glad you did; I'm excited for you.*
• *I got really angry today because someone at work took advantage of me.*	*I really regret that happened; I'm sad you don't sense more appreciation and respect at work.*
• *I felt embarrassed when I was the last one chosen for the baseball team.*	*I know that really hurt; I'm sorry it happened.*
• *I felt overwhelmed today; I've got too much going on.*	*Let's have a relaxing visit, and maybe I can encourage and support you in some way. It sounds as if you may be feeling somewhat alone in the midst of all that's going on, and I'd like to help.*
• *I was so happy to have lunch with a friend I haven't seen in years.*	*I'm glad that worked out for you; I'm sure you enjoyed the time.*

All relationships can be enriched through emotional expression: couples can emotionally connect daily, parents can take a daily "emotional vital signs" check on each child, and singles can check in with a journeymate every day. If we don't frequently experience emotional attunement, painful emotions can begin to accumulate. If we remain alone in our anxieties, fears tend to mount. If we remain alone with feelings of disappointment, discouragement sets in. If anger is allowed to fester, bitterness can develop. Likewise, if we are happy, but have no one to share with, our joy may be short-lived and not fully enjoyed.

Describe the last time you genuinely connected emotionally with another person and you both expressed and responded to each other emotionally?

_____

_____

_____

3. Emotional expression and responding cannot be experienced alone; God has given us both himself and other humans to properly process our emotions.

With all due respect to "man's best friend," pouring your heart out to your dog just won't satisfy your emotional needs. Neither will listening to talk shows, talking to yourself, writing your thoughts in a journal, or crying yourself to sleep. We must process our emotions with God and with other people. The Old Testament Psalms are filled with the psalmist's emotional heart-cries to God, and not once do we find this openness and vulnerability discouraged by God. He longs to hear from our hearts as we declare our dependency and faith. Not only can we share with God, but he has also given us human relationships by which we can be blessed through vulnerable sharing.

4. Emotional expression and responding can be accomplished both individually and in groups.

While emotional responding is often done "one on one," a deep sense of ministry is felt when the body of Christ emotionally responds—corporately—to an individual's expressed needs. For instance,

- When an entire family mourns with little brother because he didn't make the team,
- When a local church rejoices with a young couple over the birth of a baby,
- When a Bible-Study group comforts a fellow member over the death of a loved one,

...these are precious and profound times of body ministry.

When was the last time you saw emotional expression and responding in a group setting?

_____

_____

_____

When someone is sad, we often think that we need to cheer her up. But actually, the opposite is true. We need to be sad with her.

5. As we consider our loved ones, family and friends, we should anticipate times when emotional expression and responding will be needed in their lives and be ready to minister to them.

In addition to the fact that emotional responding is usually needed on a daily basis, we all experience "emotionally charged" times when feelings run deep and strong, times when we're especially vulnerable, times when emotional responding is desperately needed. It's impossible, for example, to read about the last few days of Jesus' life and not realize that these were emotionally demanding hours. For us, these times might include the following:

- A child approaching a new school year, new friends, or new activities.
- The days before major surgery, significant meetings, or important events.
- The first days after a major life change such as a new job, new church, or a move to a new city.
- When a dating couple breaks up.
- Before and after someone participates in an important athletic event, musical concert, or other major event.
- Before and after an employee review, a major presentation, or project deadline.
- After the death of a loved one.

As we anticipate these times in the lives of our loved ones, we can be particularly sensitive to being available, asking the right questions, and spending time to deal properly with the emotions of these stressful events.

Identify some future times when your family and friends might need a good dose of emotional expression and responding, and write them down.

---

6. When two people minister to each other through emotional expression and responding, "who goes first" can be determined by several factors.

When two friends meet, a priority should be for them to respond emotionally to one another—to enter into each other's emotional world and to respond appropriately. But who should enter whose world first? Here are two guidelines:

1. If one person is feeling painful emotions and the other person is feeling positive emotions, the one who is hurting should be encouraged to share first. For instance, consider this scenario:

> Mike has had a tough day at the office. Mary, his wife, has had a wonderful day shopping with friends. At 6:30 p.m. they meet at the front door. It's immediately obvious who's wounded and weary and who's wonderful and well.

The question is, who should enter whose world first? Should Mike rejoice with Mary first or should Mary mourn with Mike first? Probably the latter because it will be hard for Mike to truly rejoice with Mary until he is able to deal with his own pain.

When emotional responding is properly administered, the person who is hurting may soon feel enough relief to then properly respond to someone else.

So if Mary will minister to Mike first (*I can really sense you've had a hard day, and I'd like to hear about it; I want to comfort you in your discouragement because I love you.*), he will then be better able to rejoice with her (*I'm thrilled you had a fun time with your friend; it's been a while since you spent time with her.*).

2. "Who goes first" may be determined by spiritual servant-hood.

As an act of unselfishness, a husband might let his wife share first, a parent will encourage his or her child to go first, and a friend will prefer others over himself or herself (Philippians 2:4, Romans 12:10).

A mother's testimony about emotionally connecting with her children

The Lord blessed us with two children, a boy and a girl, born two years apart. I'm not sure exactly what prompted me to do this, but from the time they were infants, every night I would go into each child's room, sit down on his or her bed, and ask two questions, "What was the happiest thing that happened to you today?" and "What was the saddest thing that happened to you today?"

When they shared the happy emotions I simply rejoiced with them. When they shared their painful experiences, I comforted them.

It became a nightly ritual that both children cherished. I would go to my daughter's room first since she was the youngest and needed to go to sleep first. If I lingered a long time in my daughter's room, my son would inevitably inquire, "Mom, when are you coming to my room?"

Even after my son went to college, when he came home for the holidays he expected our nightly conversation. Here I am, asking my 21-year-old son, "Sweetheart, what was the happiest thing that happened to you today? What was the saddest thing that happened to you today?" But he still treasured those times of emotionally connecting.

My children were, and still are, such good kids. They are emotionally healthy, spiritually sensitive, and enjoy close relationships.

Until I heard the teaching on emotional responding, I never realized that what I was doing every evening with each child was simply experiencing Romans 12:15—I rejoiced with them as they rejoiced, I mourned with them as they mourned.

Discussion questions (Discuss these issues in your group or with your journeymate.)

1. What was the most interesting concept in this chapter?
2. Why is it difficult for us to deal with our emotions *alone*?
3. Why are we often more willing to attune emotionally with children than with adults?
4. Although some people may not be adept at articulating how they're feeling, we can learn to identify how they're feeling by listening with our ears, eyes, and heart. One rule of thumb used in communications research is that 90% or more of an emotional message is nonverbal. What are some examples of emotional, nonverbal communication?
5. Look again at the two formulas on page 15. How can the end result of both formulas be the same (feeling blessed) even though the equations seem vastly different?
6. If time allows, read and process the *Emotional Responding Learning Activity* that is located in the Facilitator's Guide.

Journeymate time (Discuss these issues with your journeymate.)

1. Share with your journeymate your responses to the fill-in-the-blank sections in this chapter.
2. A particularly important time to engage in emotional expression/responding is when family members or friends first come home from work and school. The first four or five minutes of greeting one another are very important. In your household, how are these critical times usually handled? Do you emotionally attune with one another?
3. What was the strongest emotion you felt this week? Share this with your journeymate.

Homework (To be completed before the next meeting.)

1. Practice emotional responding with someone other than your journeymate and record your encounters here.

What emotional expression did you observe in someone? [Ex. *My son came home from school really discouraged. My friend called, and she was elated that she was accepted into graduate school.*]

_____

_____

How did you respond? [Ex. *I took the time to listen to my son, and then I empathized with him and comforted him. I rejoiced with my friend over the phone, and took her to lunch the next day just to celebrate.*]

_____

_____

2. Read and process Chapter 3.

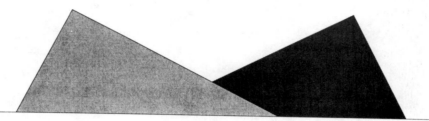

Chapter Summary

1. Empathy is the ability to enter into another person's emotional world and respond with compassion. It goes beyond sympathy, which is simply the mental awareness of the general plight of another person but with no sacrificial sharing in what she is feeling.

2. Emotional attunement is responding to another person's emotional expressions *with the same general type of emotion.*

3. All emotions can be grouped into two categories: potentially painful and potentially positive. Romans 12:15 teaches us how to "attune" to these two groups of emotions: "Rejoice with those who rejoice and mourn with those who mourn" (Romans 12:15).

4. Emotional responding is an important life skill that we must develop.

The Emotional Cup

Painful emotions are inevitable. We live in a fallen world, we're surrounded by fallen people, and we ourselves are fallen. It's not a matter of *if* we'll get hurt; it's just an issue of *when*. A significant question then, is, "What happens to the painful emotions that we experience?" Perhaps your child is embarrassed at school, or you're belittled at work. Do these emotions "go in one ear and out the other"? Do they affect us during the day but dissipate while we sleep? Do they eventually dissolve with time?

Painful emotions, unless properly dealt with, stay with us. It's been said that emotions that are buried, are buried alive. And not only do they linger, they accumulate.

To demonstrate how emotions can accumulate, we use an illustration called the *emotional cup*. It is a picture of what can happen when painful emotions are left unresolved. As with all analogies, the comparisons are not exact, but the illustration will help explain certain aspects of human emotionality.

Imagine pouring water into an 8—oz. Styrofoam coffee cup. The cup has a limited capacity so the water accumulates until the cup is full, and when more water is added, the water overflows, causing spillage.

Now picture having an inner "emotional cup." Every time you experience a painful emotion, it's as if your cup is being filled up. The unresolved emotions begin to accumulate and eventually you reach capacity, but life keeps pouring in painful emotions. Soon the emotions "spill over" and you begin to display unhealthy symptoms.

> There is, in fact, a part of the brain that controls our emotions; it is called the amygdala. "The brain has two memory systems, one for ordinary facts (neocortex) and one for emotionally charged ones (amygdala). The amygdala is the specialist for emotional matters. It acts as a storehouse of emotional memory, and thus of significance itself; life without the amygdala is a life stripped of personal meanings." Goldman, *Emotional Intelligence*, 1995

In other words, strong emotions (hurt, anger, fear), if not properly processed, begin to accumulate and our emotional capacity can become maxed out. Unfortunately, even when our cup is full, life keeps pouring in painful emotions, and we soon display unpleasant signs of "spillage."

Refer to the emotional cup diagram on the next page as we briefly discuss how our cup can become filled to overflowing. We'll discuss each painful emotion in more detail in subsequent chapters.

What's Filling Your Emotional Cup?

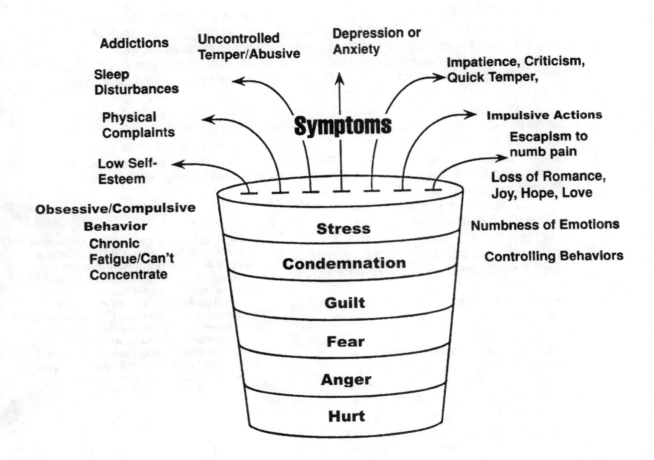

Addictions

Uncontrolled Temper/Abusive

Depression or Anxiety

Impatience, Criticism, Quick Temper,

Sleep Disturbances

Physical Complaints

Symptoms

Impulsive Actions

Escapism to numb pain

Low Self-Esteem

Loss of Romance, Joy, Hope, Love

Obsessive/Compulsive Behavior

Numbness of Emotions

Chronic Fatigue/Can't Concentrate

Controlling Behaviors

Stress

Condemnation

Guilt

Fear

Anger

Hurt

You Can Only "Hold" So Much Emotion

Our emotional cups can become filled with painful emotions

Hurt is placed at the bottom of the cup because it is usually the initial painful emotion we feel. Hurt is a general term that has many derivatives—embarrassment, rejection, loneliness, betrayal, abandonment, neglect, etc. Hurt, of course, is inevitable. Jesus confirmed this truth when he said, "In this world you will have trouble" (John 16:32).

The second emotion from the bottom is **anger**. It is a by-product of hurt; when we are hurt we often get angry. For many of us, anger is so automatic we seldom consciously recognize the hurt feelings that prompted the anger. Because it is painful to focus on our hurts, we often hide our hurt by turning outward and becoming angry at others. Anger can take many forms (impatience, a quick temper) and we often display our anger in passive-aggressive ways (procrastination, silence, sarcasm, or avoidance).

Initially, anger can be a positive emotion. It can alert us to the fact that we have been hurt; but unresolved anger can escalate into hatred and bitterness and become sin.

Unresolved hurt can also produce **fear**. Whereas anger is oriented toward the

Primary Emotions

In this book we'll concentrate on the six primary painful emotions that are listed inside the cup. Although there are many other painful emotions, they are usually derivatives of or combinations of the primary ones. Just as all colors are derived from three primary colors (blue, red, yellow), these six emotions represent the basis for most other painful emotions.

past, ("I'm angry that I was hurt") fear is future–oriented, ("I'm afraid that I'll be hurt again"). Fear, if unresolved, can lead to behavioral problems such as withdrawal (avoiding situations that might expose you to new hurt); perfectionism (a perfect performance will reduce your chance of failure and hurt); control (you minimize chances for pain by being in charge); and addictions (trying to numb the pain and fear).

Guilt enters our cup when we hurt or violate someone else. Guilt can be related to our hurt in that we often retaliate against the person who has hurt us, ("You hurt me, I'll hurt you") but it can also simply be the result of my having violated someone (*I was impatient toward my spouse. I was disrespectful of my daughter. I told a lie to my co-worker.*) Initially, guilt is a good emotion. When we offend someone we *should* feel guilty, but God never intended for guilt to remain in our cup. If it does, it will adversely affect us.

Thoughts and feelings of **false guilt** occur when we accept responsibility for hurtful or sinful actions that we were not responsible for (*I was sexually abused as a child; it must be my fault because I didn't try to stop it. Dad just walked out on Mom; it's probably my fault because he's been yelling at me a lot lately.*)

Condemnation is, perhaps, the most complicated emotion with which we struggle. Condemnation causes us to feel badly about ourselves. It can come from many sources and is often difficult to recognize. Condemnation is built on lies which undermine our worth and value as a person (*I'm just a worthless person. I can't do anything right.*)

Stress can also accumulate in our emotional cup. Whereas a certain amount of stress can be good, if we are overly stressed for an extended period of time, it can be detrimental.

As you reflect on your own emotional cup, which of the painful emotions do you most often struggle with?

How do these emotions affect your life?

_____

_____

Emotional "Spillage": Symptoms of a Full Cup

Over time, these painful, unresolved emotions can accumulate in our emotional cups and eventually we become "maxed out"—our cups are full. But life continues to pour painful emotions into our cups, and we soon display signs of *spillage*.

Spillage

Spillage is different for each individual. When our emotional cups are full we may exhibit symptoms such as these:

- depression
- anxiety
- chronic low self-esteem
- low sexual desire

Or, in order to avoid our pain, we may try to escape into behaviors like these:

- drugs
- alcohol
- pornography
- TV
- hobbies
- work
- shopping
- sports
- the Internet
- music
- computers

A full emotional cup may affect us physically; we may display physical symptoms such as the following:

- high blood pressure
- lower back pain
- skin rashes
- migraine headaches
- stomachaches
- chronic fatigue

The Center for Disease Control and Prevention states unequivocally that 80% of our medical expenditures are now stress-related.

A full emotional cup may lead to the following:

- sleep disorders - we sleep too much; we can't sleep enough

- eating disorders - we eat too much; we don't eat enough

We may have problems with impulse control; we may

- become controlling of others
- struggle with temper control and outbursts of anger

Which of these symptoms do you struggle with?

_____

_____

We often spend a lot of time and resources trying to manipulate and eradicate our symptoms. We may even succeed in "controlling" some of them, but if the underlying problems are not addressed, we'll simply exchange one symptom for another.

- *I've finally disciplined myself to lose weight, but now I sleep too much.*
- *I'm no longer addicted to drugs, but now I'm trapped in pornography.*
- *I no longer try to escape into T.V., but now I spend hours on the Internet.*

The concept of the emotional cup will help us minister effectively to others.

When we see symptoms of "spillage" in other people, we are often tempted to address just the symptoms (*Stop watching so much T.V. Stop yelling at the kids. Would you please lose weight? Take some more medicine for your headache.*). Instead, we should look beneath the symptoms and minister to the root issues. Otherwise, we'll end up simply trying to "manage" symptoms, which is an endless and futile pursuit.

Secondary emotions that are often associated with the primary emotions

Hurt – embarrassment, neglect, grief, sorrow, rejection, loneliness

Anger – outrage, resentment, bitterness, wrath, indignation, irritability, hatred

Fear – anxiety, apprehension, nervousness, dread, fright, consternation, concern

Guilt – regret, contrition, sorrow, remorse, chagrin

Condemnation – shame, embarrassment, humiliation, scorn

Stress – feeling overwhelmed, hopelessness, nervousness

Painful results of a full emotional cup

1. We suffer emotionally.

Look again at the emotional cup diagram. Let's be honest. That's not a pretty picture. When we are emotionally distraught—overcome with hurt, anger, fear, guilt, condemnation, and stress—we're miserable.

A testimony of how a full cup can adversely affect our lives

When I was twelve years old, my father left us. He just walked out. Although it hurt me a lot, I never really talked to anyone about it. My brothers and sisters were younger than me, so I didn't want to talk to them; my mother was devastated and consumed with her own pain, and I was too embarrassed to talk to my friends because I didn't know how they would react. So I just stuffed it and tried to forget it. But years later I began to realize that it was still an unresolved issue in my life.

Several years into marriage, I felt a constant sense of anger, which simmered just below the surface. At first I became pretty adept at controlling my anger, but occasionally I would yell at my kids. At times, I totally lost control. I also became very insecure and anxious about my relationship with my husband, Jerry. He had always been a loving husband, very dedicated and faithful, but whenever we would have a quarrel or disagreement, deep inside I was afraid that he was going to leave me. This fear caused me to be overly jealous and controlling. It almost ruined our marriage.

All through the years I have been faithful to read my Bible and attend church; I was believing right and trying to behave right, but something wasn't working. I tried to "claim" the abundant life that Christ had provided, but it was very elusive.

Then one day, I saw the emotional cup diagram and realized that there was a lot of anger in my cup. The anger was directly related to the hurt I sustained when my father abandoned our family. The unresolved hurt had also produced fear in me; I was anxious that it would happen to me again, this time as a wife. And there was probably some guilt in my cup because I had decided never to talk to my father even though he had tried to contact me on several occasions.

Yes, I can testify that those painful emotions don't just go away with time. They stay with us and can rob us of day-to-day joy.

2. We are unable to feel positive emotions.

If our emotional capacity is filled with painful emotions, we will have difficulty enjoying positive emotions such as joy, contentment, happiness and romance. If our emotional cup is filled with hurt, anger, fear, and condemnation, it's not surprising that we'll have difficulty feeling romantic, fulfilled, or affirmed.

In John 10:10, Jesus said that one reason he came was that we might have an abundant, full, and meaningful life. But in the same verse, he warns us that the enemy wants to steal from us, kill, and destroy us. How does the enemy steal from us the abundant life that Christ has provided?

Consider this truth: There are only three tenses of time - past, present, and future. If we are to experience the abundant life that Christ promised, we must experience it in the present. We may have experienced some of it in the past, but when we did, it was in the present. We have the hope of experiencing abundant life in the future, but when we do, it will also be in the present. If the enemy can keep us angry about our past and anxious about the future, he will rob us of *present* abundance. For instance, it's hard to be abundantly happy and exceedingly angry at the same time. Likewise, it's difficult to be cheerful and content if we're incapacitated with anxiety. That's one reason why we must deal with what's in our cup. It's naive to say, "Yeah, I was hurt, but that was years ago. It doesn't matter now." It does matter now.

Quite often, when couples come in for counseling, one of the partners will say, "I just don't love my spouse any more. The truth is, I don't feel anything. I just feel numb." These statements are indicative of a full cup. When someone is emotionally "maxed out," these feelings are neither surprising nor uncommon.

3. Our personal spillage will adversely affect all of our relationships.

Unfortunately, when our own emotional cup is full, it not only adversely affects us; it also adversely affects all our relationships.

- Our fear will cause us to be controlling of others.
- Unresolved anger will cause us to say hurtful words to those we love.
- Guilt will hinder our willingness to share our lives with others.

Imagine the pain and confusion of a marriage in which both husband and wife have full cups; they will probably have marital problems, not just because of marriage issues (communication, finances, etc.) but because of how their individual struggles affect each other.

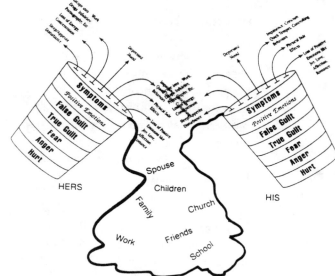

How have your symptoms hurt those who are close to you? (For instance: *My escaping into work hurts my spouse. I often become impatient with my children.*)

_____

_____

_____

Can a group of people have a "corporate emotional cup"?

We've been applying the emotional cup illustration to our individual lives, but does it have implications to groups of people? Can a society suffer from corporate anger and guilt and begin to exhibit spillage? Can a church's emotional cup be filled with anger, fear, and guilt? The following testimony would indicate that groups of people do indeed have a "corporate" emotional cup.

A pastor's testimony about how a church can have a full cup.

Several years ago I was called to be pastor of a church. We had been there only a few months when I noticed some odd things happening. The church leaders were inordinately controlling of the church's finances; they acted as if they didn't trust me. Every expenditure, even the small ones, had to be approved by the entire finance committee. It took an act of Congress just to get some benevolence money for a needy family. And the church seemed overly suspicious of my personal life; they wanted to know where I was and who I was with all the time. It was hard not to take all this personally, but I soon discovered what was causing all the suspicion and distrust.

Their former pastors had repeatedly abused the church. My predecessor had an affair with his secretary, the man before him had absconded with church funds, and the pastor before him was also caught in sexual immorality. By the time I got there, the church was hurt, angry, and suspicious.

My wife and I had taught on the emotional cup in our previous church so I knew that an individual could get "filled up" with hurt, anger and fear - but could a church? It was painfully obvious that it could.

Over the next several months we started to share with the church the same truths about being set free from emotional bondage that we would teach individuals. We began the healing process with the church leaders at a weekend retreat and then ministered to the whole church during the Sunday evening services. A lot of healing took place, and eventually the symptoms subsided.

4. Our emotional cup goes with us wherever we go.

Obviously, our emotional cup is within us, so it accompanies us wherever we go. In any given situation, we may think that the relational chaos we are experiencing is purely circumstantial and if we move to a different environment, the chaos will cease. But soon after moving, the same problems begin to surface, and we are tempted to move again.

For instance, a person may move from one tumultuous job experience to another hoping to find peace, only to discover that the conflict comes from within, and thus the emotional turmoil is also moving from job to job.

In a marriage, after years of turmoil, one partner may decide to leave the relationship, hoping to find peace. But unfortunately, our emotional cup goes with us - we don't leave it behind with the abandoned relationship; consequently, it will adversely affect our new relationships.

Positive results of emptying the emotional cup

1. Painful symptoms may subside.

Painful symptoms cannot always be directly related to painful emotions in the cup. For instance, depression may be the result of emotional trauma, or it may be genetic and/or bio-chemical in nature. Lower back pain may be caused by emotional turmoil, but it could also be the result of having strained your back. Cause and effect relationships are sometimes difficult to establish. But often, painful symptoms *can* be directly correlated to unresolved pain.

To the extent that symptoms *are* directly related to painful emotions in the cup, these symptoms will, over time, begin to subside as the painful emotions are properly dealt with. We use the phrase "over time" because some symptoms can become ingrained habits, which may take a longer period of time to break. For example, someone may struggle with alcoholism as a way of escaping from painful emotions, but even after the emotions are properly dealt with, the temptation to drink may still be there simply because it is now a habit which has become a physical addiction.

2. We'll be able to enjoy positive emotions.

Once our cup is emptied of painful emotions, we'll have the capacity to enjoy positive ones. Feelings of love, acceptance, encouragement, affirmation, romance, and hope can once again be experienced.

General principles for emptying our emotional cup

1. God wants us to be set free.
There are many different opinions as to God's will regarding physical healing. Some Christians believe God wants to heal everyone all the time. Others believe differently.

But though there are different opinions regarding physical healing, there is a general consensus regarding inward healing. God really does want us to be free from the shackles that entangle the soul. This is important to understand and embrace because it will give us hope.

2. God's word has the answer.
"Now that you have purified yourselves by obeying the truth…" (1 Peter 1:22).

God's word is not primarily a book of science (we wouldn't expect to learn all there is to know about physics in the Bible), although when it speaks scientifically, it is correct. Likewise, the Bible is not primarily a book of history, although when it speaks historically, it is correct. But we do believe that the Bible teaches us all we need to know about relationships—human and divine. It teaches us everything we need to know about developing intimacy in relationships and how to heal damaged ones.

3. There is a unique, biblical antidote for each painful emotion.
God's word prescribes a unique solution for each problem, but we must match the correct antidote with each peculiar emotion. We must "rightly divide" the Word (2 Timothy 2:15).

Testimony on how specific problems require specific solutions

Several years ago my family went on a mission trip to the Ukraine. Although we were stationed in a rather large city, there were limited medical facilities, and prescription drugs were unavailable. Half way through the trip my daughter got bronchitis. Miraculously, we found a Christian doctor, but he had no medicine. Fortunately, there was a man in our group who, before leaving for the Ukraine, had gone to his doctor's office and gotten a sack full of various samples of medicine.

After the doctor examined my daughter and diagnosed the problem, we dumped the bag of medicine out on the table. The doctor picked up the samples one at a time and studied their application. There was medicine for high blood pressure, migraine headaches, thyroid problems, but nothing specifically for bronchitis. Eventually, he found an antibiotic that, although it wasn't specifically for bronchitis, was close enough. My daughter took the medicine and improved quickly.

How foolish it would have been for us just to reach into the bag, randomly select a medicine, give it to my daughter and expect her to get better. It would have been dangerously naïve to think that just any medicine would help her specific illness.

But we often take a haphazard approach to "prescribing" the word of God. When ministering to someone who struggles with fear, we may say, "Just read the Bible every night before you go to bed." When someone is angry we may casually suggest, "The Psalmist David often got angry; why don't you just read the Psalms?"

It's important to understand that the Bible presents a unique solution to each individual painful emotion.

- The antidote for guilt will not relieve hurt.
- The cure for hurt will not remove false guilt.
- The same thing that will soothe our anger does not placate our fear.
- The same thing that removes guilt will not displace condemnation.

The next eight chapters explain in detail the particular biblical antidotes for each painful emotion. Let's pause here to take a pre-test. Indicate below which antidote you think applies to each emotion. (Connect with a line.)

Fear	Mourn/comfort
False guilt	Forgive
Anger	Know truth
Hurt	Perfect love
Condemnation	Confess
Guilt	Faith

4. We must *experience* biblical truth to be set free.

Just mentally knowing biblical truth will not set us free; we must experience it. According to 1 Peter 1:22 we are "purified by obeying the truth."

For instance, in Chapter 7, we'll discuss how confession relieves guilt (1 John 1:9, James 5:16). But it's possible to study confession (memorize verses, study them in the original Greek language, quote them out loud several times a day), yet still feel guilty. We won't be delivered from guilt until we *experience* confession. And we'll discover that these truths must be experienced in *relationships*; we cannot experience them in isolation.

In the following chapters, we'll discuss in detail the biblical antidote for each of the painful emotions that can fill our cups.

Discussion questions (Discuss these issues in your group or with your journeymate.)

1. What was the most interesting concept in this chapter?
2. In your community, what types of "spillage" do you see among society? In an attempt to resolve these issues, do we usually address the causes or just the symptoms?
3. It has been said that Jesus "looked beyond people's deeds and ministered to their needs." How does this apply to the emotional cup illustration and our ministry to others?
4. Read again, the mother's testimony recorded on page 21. How did her bedtime routine with her children help empty their emotional cups?
5. If time allows, process the *Emotional Cup Learning Activity* that is located in the Facilitator's Guide.

Journeymate time (Discuss these issues with your journeymate.)

1. Share with your journeymate the results of last week's homework.
2. Share with your journeymate your responses to the fill-in-the-blank sections for this week's lesson.
3. Which of the painful emotions and symptoms of a full cup did you most often observe in your family while you were growing up?
4. [For those who are married] When you got married, you probably hoped that you and your partner would come to the marriage altar with empty cups. But in reality, both of you probably came with partially or totally full cups. How have your individual struggles adversely affected your marriage relationship? [For single adults] When you became an adult you might have thought that you automatically left behind childhood issues, but unless properly resolved, the painful issues of childhood can continue to affect us adversely as adults. Share with your journeymate some of these issues.

Homework (To be completed before the next meeting.)

1. This week, try to notice when a painful emotion is deposited into your cup. (For instance, *My mother-in-law really insulted me in front of my children—that hurt. I was fearful about some medical problems I'm having.*)

Record the incidents here:

_____

_____

_____

2. Read Chapter 4 and complete the fill-in-the-blank sections.

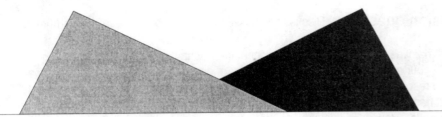

Chapter Summary

1. Painful emotions must be properly dealt with, or they will accumulate and lead to unhealthy and painful symptoms.

2. Having a full emotional cup will adversely affect us as individuals, and it will also adversely affect our relationships.

3. God wants us to be healed from painful emotions and God's word has the antidote for each painful emotion. It is not enough merely to understand biblical truth; we must *experience* biblical truth in the context of relationships to be set free.

Freedom from Hurt

"Where have you been?" the mother demanded.
The little girl replied, "On my way home, I met a friend who was crying
because she had broken her doll."
"Oh," said her mother, "then you stopped to help her fix the doll?"
"Oh, no," replied the little girl, "I stopped to help her cry."

Hurt is the first emotion we'll discuss because it is the most frequently experienced painful emotion and because, if not properly managed, it can lead to other painful emotions such as anger, fear, and condemnation.

Characteristics of Hurt

1. Hurt is inevitable.

Jesus said, "In this world you will have trouble" (John 16:33). His statement wasn't a threat, just a fact of life. It's not a matter of *if* we're going to be hurt, but rather *when* we will be hurt and more importantly, what are we going to do about it?

2. Hurt comes from various sources.

Hurt can come from many sources: circumstances (illness, accidents); family members (spouse, children, parents, in-laws, grandparents); friends; enemies. It seems ironic, but sometimes those closest to us can hurt us more frequently and more deeply than others can. This is because we are around them more often, and our expectation level is higher towards those we love.

3. Hurt can take many forms.

There are many synonyms for hurt:
I was *disappointed* that my co-worker didn't finish his part of our project.
I was *embarrassed* when I tripped and fell in front of my classmates.
I was *offended* at the racist remark that was made.
I felt *betrayed* when my friend spoke against me.
I was *frustrated* when my car wouldn't start.
I felt *abandoned* when my spouse left me.
I felt *sad* on the first anniversary of my mother's death.

4. There are different sizes of hurt.

There are different degrees of hurt:

5¢ - "When I was at lunch today, I felt embarrassed because I spilt ketchup on my tie."

$5 – "I had a flat tire today and had to change it in the rain."

$500 – "My company is downsizing; I got laid off today."

$5,000 – "When I was 12 years old, my father abandoned our family."

While some hurts are obviously more serious than others, we shouldn't dismiss any hurt, regardless of how insignificant it may seem.

5. We all have unique areas of vulnerability and sensitivity.

We all have unique emotional "soft spots" - areas in which we are particularly sensitive and vulnerable to hurt. One person may be very sensitive about his family of origin; another may be particularly susceptible to hurt in the area of physical appearance. One individual may be "thin-skinned" about having not graduated from high school, whereas someone else may take pride in the fact that, although he didn't graduate from high school, he became successful.

This fact should deepen our level of sensitivity to others. We should discover each person's peculiar areas of vulnerability and be careful to consider them. Until we are able to identify those particular areas, we should be careful to avoid saying anything that might be offensive.

Furthermore, when someone expresses a hurt, we should never say, "That shouldn't have hurt you, you're just being too sensitive." If someone is hurt, he's hurt. Don't argue over whether or not the individual *should* have been hurt, this is a very subjective issue. The fact is, he is.

What are some areas of your life in which you are particularly vulnerable to hurt?

6. The antidote for hurt is always the same.

Regardless of the *source* of hurt, the *form* the hurt takes, and the *size* of the hurt, the antidote is always the same. This is good news because otherwise, think of the complex solution grid that we would have to negotiate if there were a different solution depending on source (If someone is hurt at school, treat it one way; if someone is hurt by a family member, another solution is needed); form (If someone is embarrassed, she needs _____; if she's feeling rejected, she needs _____); and size (If it's a small hurt respond one way; if it's a mid-sized hurt, treat it differently).

Later in this chapter we'll discover that there is only one antidote for hurt: comfort. And while this seems to be an overly simplistic solution, it is, nevertheless, sufficient.

Jesus Experienced All Dimensions of Hurt

It's important and comforting to know that Jesus experienced every dimension of hurt and sadness. That's why he is described as "A man of sorrows, and familiar with suffering" (Isaiah 53:3). During his earthly ministry, he experienced all these hurts:

Physical pain: Fasted for 40 days, his beard was plucked out, he was beaten and crucified.

Emotional pain:

- Rejected in his hometown - Mark 6:2-4
- Called demon-possessed by the Pharisees - John 10:20
- Rejected by his family - Mark 3:20-21
- Insulted by his disciples - Matthew 26:6-9
- Disappointed by Philip - John 14:6-9
- Offended in the upper room at the last supper - Luke 22:24
- Unsupported in the Garden of Gethsemane - Mark 14:32-40
- Embarrassed on the cross - John 19:23
- Mocked - Luke 23:36
- Cursed - Luke 23:39

Spiritual pain:

- Rejected by his Father - Mark 15:33-34

Hebrews 4:15 states that "We do not have a high priest who is unable to sympathize with our weaknesses." Jesus suffered in all ways, so he understands how we feel and is ready to minister to us in our pain.

Please Explain!

Question - How can you say Jesus suffered in every way and is therefore able to empathize with my pain? I went through a grueling divorce several years ago, Jesus never experienced that.

Answer - There are innumerable ways in which we can be hurt (divorce, bankruptcy, illness, etc.), but there is a limited number of emotions that we feel as a result of being hurt. Obviously, Jesus did not experience all the specific ways in which one can be hurt (for instance, you correctly mentioned the pain of divorce); but through his own set of hurtful experiences he did experience the painful emotions that are common to all people. For instance, what emotions did you experience before, during, and after your divorce? Anger? Rejection? Abandonment? Jesus suffered the pain of these emotions as well, just through different circumstances.

This is an important principle to remember when we minister to others because we may think that we can't adequately minister to someone unless we've "walked in his shoes." For instance, one may ask, "How can I minister to someone who has just lost a child if I never have?" But on a foundational level, we can identify with the feelings of loss, confusion, and pain.

Hurt can lead to other painful emotions

If not properly dealt with, hurt can lead to other painful emotions such as anger, fear, or condemnation. Often, these second-generation emotions come so quickly that they appear to be initial/primary emotions, but they are usually the result of being hurt.

Hurt can lead to anger

When we are hurt, it's quite normal to become immediately angry. In the next chapter we'll discuss the fact that initially, there's nothing wrong with becoming angry—as long as it is properly expressed and dealt with. When we feel angry it's important to realize that most often, underneath the anger is hurt; consequently, the only way to deal properly with the anger is first to deal with the underlying hurt.

We can see the hurt/anger connection in the life of Jesus as recorded in Mark 3:5: "Jesus, grieved in his spirit (hurt), looked at them in anger."

Let's use a hypothetical story to illustrate how hurt can lead to anger, fear, and condemnation.

Setting - Susan works for a large public relations firm. During a staff meeting, Tom, her boss, throws her a curve.

> Tom - Susan, I'm taking you off the Cortex account and putting Jerry in charge.
> Susan - Tom, I've worked that account for two months; I'm just now finalizing a strategic plan.
> Tom - I know, but this is going to work out better; I'm assigning you to the Sebring account.
> Susan - Sebring! Aren't they located in Minneapolis?
> Tom - Yes.
> Susan - So I'm going to be making regular trips to Minnesota?
> Tom - I guess so.
> Susan - Can we talk about this?
> Tom - Not really.

[Later at home, Bob, Susan's husband, asks her about her day.]

> Bob - Hi Susan, how did your day go?
> Susan - You don't want to know.
> Bob – What happened?
> Susan – Tom gave the Cortex account to Jerry just when I was about to finalize a plan. Now Jerry will get all the credit. Not only that, but Tom gave me the new Sebring portfolio so I'll have to start from scratch. And on top of that, I'll also have to go to Minneapolis once a week. I'm so mad at Tom.
> Bob - I am so tired of Tom treating you like that. I feel like calling him myself; somebody needs to set him straight.
> Susan - It upset me so much; I left the office early and just drove around for several hours.

Susan was deeply hurt by her boss's actions. But anger came so quickly that perhaps she didn't realize she had been hurt. Unfortunately, Bob's response only exacerbated her anger.

When was the last time you got angry?

_____

_____

_____

What might have been an underlying hurt?

_____

_____

Hurt can lead to fear

If hurt is not properly dealt with, it can also lead to fear. Whereas anger is directed to the past (I'm angry that I got hurt in the past.), fear is future-oriented (I'm afraid that I'll get hurt again.). Let's revisit Susan's situation and see how her unhealed hurt could affect her perspective on the future.

Setting - Six weeks have passed since Susan's incident with her boss. She and Bob visit one morning at the breakfast table.

Bob - Susan, you've been really quiet lately. Is anything wrong?
Susan - I'm just having a difficult time at work.
Bob – What's bothering you?
Susan – I'm having a hard time focusing on the Sebring case.
Bob - Is it the travel that's wearing you down?
Susan - I don't think so.
Bob - Then what is it?
Susan – I'm getting to the same place on this account that I was in the Cortex account when Tom jerked it away from me and gave it to Jerry. I guess I'm afraid he'll do it again.
Bob - Has he said anything to make you feel that way?
Susan - No.
Bob - Then why are you worried?
Susan – I'm not sure, but it's all I can think about. Sometimes at the office I just sit at my desk like a deer staring at the headlights of a car, frozen with fright.

Susan is struggling with the fear of what might happen in the future, and her fear is spawned by the unresolved hurt from the past.

In what areas of your life are you apprehensive about the future?

_____

_____

What past hurts may be contributing to these feelings of apprehension and fear?

_____

_____

[Note: in chapter six we'll discuss the fact that there are several different sources of fear; not all fear is a result of being hurt.]

Hurt can lead to feelings of condemnation

If left unresolved, hurt can also lead to feelings of condemnation. Condemnation is a debilitating sense of worthlessness. It is an attack on who we are, our self-image and self-worth. Here's how condemnation could subtly find a place in Susan's life.

Setting - Three months after her hurtful experience, Susan is still struggling.

> Susan – I'm thinking about quitting my job.
> Bob - What? Susan, I can't believe you're saying that!
> Susan - I just think it's the best thing to do. I've been thinking lately about Tom's giving the Cortex account to Jerry. It was one of our largest accounts. He probably thought I just couldn't handle it. And now I'm beginning to think he was right.
> Bob - Has he *told* you that?
> Susan - No, but I can just tell.
> Bob - How?
> Susan - I don't know, but it doesn't really matter. I've had a hard time concentrating on the Sebring case. Maybe I *have* lost my edge. There have been times when I've felt overwhelmed and out of my league. This whole incident just confirms what I've suspected all along – I'm a mediocre professional.

The hurt Susan sustained has now led to feelings of condemnation. Her self-talk, combined with lies from the enemy, has begun to undermine and weaken her self-image and her sense of worth.

What condemning thoughts do you sometimes struggle with?

_____

_____

Can you trace them to unresolved hurt?

_____

_____

Freedom from hurt

How can we empty hurt from our cup? And how can we minister to someone who has been hurt?

What to do when *you're* hurting:

1. Learn to recognize when you are hurt.

As mentioned earlier, hurt is usually the initial emotion we *experience*; but it's not always the first emotion we *express*. Because we often feel angry a millisecond after we are hurt, we tend to think, "I'm angry" instead of "I'm hurt." The truth is, both emotions are being felt and we need to deal with both; but we often deny or minimize our hurt, refusing to acknowledge it.

We may be reluctant to admit our hurt because we think it's a sign of weakness or spiritual immaturity. But it is neither. Hurt is just a common part of human experience.

2. Share your hurt with a journeymate.

Let's dissect this statement one word and phrase at a time.

Share – Your hurt with a journeymate. Don't
1. Stuff it
   > Bob – "Hi honey. How did your day go at the office?"
   > Susan – "Oh, fine."
2. Ignore it
   > Bob – "Hi honey. How did your day go at the office?"
   > Susan – "We had a pretty rough staff meeting, but that's become quite common in the past several months. What's for dinner?"
3. Minimize it
   > Bob – "Hi, honey. How did your day go at the office?"
   > Susan – "My boss was pretty ruthless in staff meeting, but everyone took a shot. Actually, others got it worse than I."

Share **your hurt**, but not your anger.

As mentioned before, we often are quick to express our anger but reluctant to share our hurt. Unfortunately, those closest to us often bear the brunt of our anger.

Bob – "Hi honey. How did your day go at the office?"
Susan – "I don't want to talk about it, okay? Just leave me alone for a while."

Share your hurt **with a journeymate**.

When you're hurting, it's not sufficient to pour your heart out to a puppy dog or to a stuffed animal. You need to share with a human being. Escaping is not an option either. If you're hurting, don't go to the television, the refrigerator or the mall. Share it with a journeymate.

Here's a suggested approach. First, tell your journeymate that you need to talk about something serious. "Bob, I really had a rough day at the office today. Sometime tonight, could we talk about it? I need to share with you how I'm feeling." Then, when the time is right, share with your journeymate what happened and how it made you feel.

3. Receive comfort.

In the following pages we'll discuss the blessing of comfort, and we'll discover that it is the primary antidote for hurt. At this point in the chapter, just understand that when comfort is given, we must *receive* it. Interestingly, when someone proffers comfort, we may feel awkward and have a difficult time receiving it. We may respond with:
- "Oh, I'll be okay."
- "Yeah, I took some hits, but my brother got it worse than I did."
- "Hey, life is tough; we all need to realize that hard times are inevitable."

Instead, we simply need to receive the comfort that is offered. Just relax, allow the comforting words to minister to you, and then verbally confirm that you have received the comfort: "Thank you for caring; your kind words mean a lot to me. I appreciate your comforting words; that's exactly what I need."

Are you uncomfortable with receiving comfort? Explain.

How to respond to *someone else* who is hurting:

1. When you know that someone is hurting, if possible, enter her physical world.

When ministering to someone who is hurting, it's best to be with her physically. While it is possible to comfort someone over the phone or in a letter, comfort is most effective when administered in person. It's also more effective to enter into *her* world. If someone is hurting, instead of saying, "Susan, it sounds as if we need to talk. Can you drop by my office this afternoon?" it would be better to say, "Susan, it sounds as if we need to talk. May I come by your office this afternoon? If that's not a good place to talk, we can go somewhere to get a cup of coffee."

2. Enter into her emotional world.

We all live in several different "worlds" simultaneously. At any given moment we are somewhere physically, emotionally, and mentally. It's obvious where someone is physically, but it's often a challenge to discover what she's thinking (her mental world) and how she's feeling (her emotional world).

When comforting someone, it is important to try to enter into her emotional world, to actually feel the same as she is feeling.

As mentioned in Chapter Two, there's a difference between sympathy and empathy. Sympathy is simply mentally identifying someone's emotional state (I understand that you just got fired from your job), whereas empathy involves not only identifying a person's emotional state but *entering into* her emotions - being sad that she is sad, rejoicing when she is happy. When you empathize with someone, you actually feel the same as she is feeling.

A testimony that illustrates empathy

I was recently with a group of men who were sharing with each other what was going on in their lives. One guy had just been fired from his job, so he was really hurting. As he shared his pain, another man in the group, who didn't even know the man who was sharing, began to weep gently. I'll never forget the look on the man's face who was sharing when he noticed that this guy was weeping for him. It was a phenomenal act of concern and empathy that this man would so feel the pain of another that he would weep for him.

3. Listen more, talk less.

A good comforter must be a good listener. The one who has been hurt should do most of the talking, and the person comforting should simply listen. Try to discern how the hurting person is *feeling*. She may spend most of the time sharing facts and details about a particular incident, but as she shares, try to discern the painful emotions she must be feeling.

Testimony about the importance of being a good listener for someone who is hurting

I always felt uncomfortable knowing what to say to someone who had just lost a loved one. Before, during, or after the funeral I would feel awkward because I didn't know what to do. Now I realize that in times like these, what people really need is just comfort.

First of all, they need for me just to be there. Secondly, they need a gentle embrace. Then they need simple words of comfort. I've learned that often, the less I say, the better. If I say too much, I'll inevitably begin to get into the area of logic and reasoning, and that will not minister comfort. Now I realize that comfort is actually a very simple but powerful ministry.

4. Offer words of comfort, accompanied by gentle affection.

When someone is hurting, she needs comfort. Comfort is an emotional, not a cerebral commodity. It is also very simple. If we try to make it complicated, we'll dilute its effectiveness. And since comfort is primarily emotional in nature, usually the fewer words spoken, the better. If we say too much, we will inevitably move into the cognitive, rational realm, which is usually counterproductive.

The "vocabulary" of comfort includes phrases like these:

- "I'm really sorry that you're hurting."
- "It hurts me that you're hurting because I love you and care for you."
- "It saddens me that you felt _____ (embarrassed, rejected, belittled). I know that must have hurt you."

When speaking words of comfort, it's also important that our *tone of voice* be complementary to what is being said. Words of comfort should be spoken gently and with compassion.

Additionally, appropriate, gentle acts of physical affection can be a wonderful complement to comforting words. Depending on the relationship, a warm embrace, a hug, holding hands, or a kiss can help communicate care and concern.

> The *vocabulary of comfort* consists of only a few words. There may be several million words in the Oxford Dictionary but only about 40-50 words qualify as comforting words. Learn those few words, and when you're comforting someone, refrain from speaking any other words.

5. Avoid unproductive responses.

When someone is hurting, she needs comfort. She doesn't need

- **Advice/instruction**
  "Let me tell you how to solve the problem."
  "Maybe next time that happens you should..."
- **Logic/reasoning**
  "Let me analyze the situation and tell you why it happened."
  "I think the reason that happened was because..."
- **Pep talk**
  "You're a winner! You'll make it through these tough times!"
  "I'm sure tomorrow will be a better day."
- **Minimize the incident**
  "Sure it hurt, but get things into perspective; there's a lot going on that's good."
  "Aren't you being overly sensitive?"
- **Anger**
  "That makes me so mad! They shouldn't get away with that!" (Angry at who caused the hurt.)
  "I'm so upset that you keep getting yourself hurt." (Angry at who got hurt.)
- **Martyr's complex**
  "I had something similar happen to me."
  "After the kind of day I had, let me tell you what hurt *really* feels like."
- **Personal fear/anxiety**
  "I'm afraid that's going to affect my life too."
- **Mr. "Fix it"**
  "I can't believe that salesman talked to you like that. I'm calling the store right now and talking to his boss."
  "I know you must have been scared when you had a flat tire on that lonely road. Tomorrow I'll take the car in and get a whole new set of tires."
- **Spiritualizing**
  "Well, you know that God will work all this out for your good."
  "Remember what Joseph said when his brothers mistreated him: 'They meant it for evil, but God meant it for good.'"
  "It's good to know that we are more than conquerors through Christ!"

Review these unproductive responses to a hurting person. Which are you most tempted to offer? *When someone is hurting, I'm often inclined to*

_____

_____

Write down a situation in which you improperly responded to someone who was hurting. (For instance, *John was really discouraged about his algebra class. Instead of comforting him I gave him advice and instruction.*)

_____

_____

_____

6. Many of these unproductive responses can actually become productive if they are engaged in *after* comfort has been ministered.

There's nothing wrong with offering advice and instruction to someone who has been hurt; it's just not the best *initial* response. *After* you have genuinely comforted someone who is hurting, he may benefit from your advice, but not before.

Likewise, there's nothing wrong with putting things in spiritual perspective (spiritualizing), fixing the problem (Mr. "Fix it"), sharing from personal experience (Martyrs' complex), or trying to figure out what happened and why it happened (logic and reasoning). But these should always come *after* you have ministered a generous dose of comfort. Prior to receiving comfort, these responses are unproductive at best, and at worst, offensive. But subsequent to adequate comfort, they can be effective.

For instance, when someone we care for is hurting, a natural tendency is to want to "fix" what went wrong.

- Your eight-year old daughter is crying because the teacher embarrassed her in front of her classmates. What parent wouldn't want to "fix" that situation: "Sweetheart, that makes me so mad. I'm going to school with you tomorrow, meet with your teacher and the principal, and get this straightened out."
- When your co-worker has been taken advantage of by a fellow employee, your typical response might be, "Let me deal with this. I'm meeting with the boss this afternoon. I'll let him know what happened, and he and I will straighten this out."
- Your friend just found out that she has cancer. You might be tempted to say, "I know the best cancer doctor in town. First thing in the morning I'll call her and get you an appointment."

But our first and most important response to a hurting person should be comfort. Perhaps at a later time and in a different setting, we can offer advice and instruction and try to "fix" what went wrong.

In this chapter, we've been using a hypothetical illustration involving Susan and her husband Bob. So far, we've shown the wrong way for Susan and Bob to deal with hurt. Now let's script out the proper way.

Bob - Hi, honey. How did your day at the office go?
Susan - Not too good; we really had a rough staff meeting. Sometime tonight I need to talk about it.
Bob - I really want to hear what happened. Could we spend some time together right after dinner?
Susan - That would be great; right now I want to go change into some comfortable clothes.

After dinner, Bob takes the initiative to lead Susan into the den where they sit together on the couch. He takes the phone off the hook; the television is off. He puts his arm around her and says

Bob - I really want to hear what happened today. It sounds as if it was a pretty rough day.

Susan - It was a terrible day. We had an explosion in the morning staff meeting, and it set the mood for the rest of the day.

Bob - Tell me what happened.

Susan – You know the Cortex case I've been working on for several months now…well, without any explanation, Tom gave the case to Jerry.

Bob - How did that make you feel?

Susan - At first, I felt betrayed. Tom knows I've poured my life into that account for months now. But then I felt embarrassed. After he made his announcement, the rest of the staff got real quiet; they knew something was wrong.

Bob - I know that must have been embarrassing. Did anyone say anything about it?

Susan - Of course not! They just sat there. Jerry had this obnoxious smirk on his face. He knows I got the short end of the stick.

Bob – So you felt taken advantage of.

Susan – Big time.

Bob - Susan, I can see now that you really did have a difficult day - actually, a terrible day. I'm really sorry all that happened. I know how hard you've worked on that account, so you must be very disappointed. That's got to hurt a lot.

Susan - Yes, it does.

Bob - I really hurt for you. It saddens me that you were embarrassed. I love you.

Susan - Thanks for caring.

The Need for Continual Comfort

Sometimes we will need continual comforting in some areas of hurt. Perhaps the hurt was extremely traumatic and/or we're continually reminded of the hurt because of natural events.

Testimony about needing continual comfort

My father died when I was 13 years old. He was my hero. My mother and others really did a good job of comforting me immediately after it happened, but I've discovered that my emotional pain resurfaces periodically and that I continue to need to be comforted over his death. For instance, when I graduated from high school, I was really sad because Dad wasn't there to see me walk across the stage. That evening, I shared it with my mom, and we cried together.

When Jeff and I got married, our wedding was a great experience, and yet, when my brother walked me down the aisle instead of my father, a tinge of sadness ran through my emotions. I shared it with Jeff the next day; he was so sweet, he just held me, told me he understood how I was feeling, and then he prayed for me. I also felt sad over my dad's death when our first child was born. Dad would have been so proud to be a grandfather. Once again, I was able to share my feelings with Jeff. This time he actually cried with me.

I'm not sure how often this will continue to happen, but I know it will. There are some hurts in life that are so significant that one large dose of comfort is just not enough. It's not a "been there, comforted that" scenario. I'm glad I'm surrounded by caring, loving family members and friends who understand this need.

The Miracle of Matthew 5:4

A wonderful healing takes place when we mourn our hurts and receive comfort. We actually end up feeling blessed that someone entered our emotional state and cared for us. This simple but profound ministry of mourning and comforting is rooted and grounded in Scripture.

The power behind this miraculous transaction is that when we mourn and comfort, we're actually experiencing a Bible verse: "Blessed are those who mourn, for they will be comforted" (Matthew 5:4).

When we rearrange the main elements of this verse, we have

Mourning + Comforting = Being Blessed!

How can we start out feeling sad and end up feeling blessed? It's a miracle from God!

Discussion Questions (Discuss these issues in your group or with your journeymate.)

1. What was the most interesting concept presented in this chapter?
2. John 11:17-37 tells the story of Jesus raising Lazarus from the dead. As Jesus approached the tomb, he saw Mary and her friends weeping. The Bible says he was "deeply moved in spirit and troubled." Then comes the shortest verse in the Bible, "Jesus wept." Why was Jesus weeping? How is this an example of empathy? What might Jesus have been tempted to say to Mary? (Consider the unproductive responses listed on page 46.)
3. If time allows, process the *Freedom from Hurt Learning Activity* that is located in the Facilitator's Guide.

Journeymate time (Discuss these issues with your journeymate.)

1. Share with your journeymate the results of your homework from last week.
2. Share with your journeymate your responses to the fill-in-the-blank sections in this week's lesson.
3. This week you probably encountered a hurting person. What was your response to him or her?
4. This week you were probably hurt or felt sad. What did you do with your hurt and sadness? If you shared it with someone, what was his or her response?
5. As you consider the emotional cup illustration, what hurt and sadness might be in your cup that you have never dealt with or perhaps that needs to be revisited? Share these areas with your journeymate and minister comfort to one another.

Homework (To be completed before the next meeting.)

1. Ask the Holy Spirit to make you more aware of people who are hurting. As you encounter them, share words of comfort. Keep a record of your encounters.

   Hurting person _____
   My response _____

   Hurting person _____
   My response _____

   Hurting person _____
   My response _____

2. This week, be aware of your own hurt and sadness; share it with your journeymate and receive comfort.

   This week I was sad about or hurt over _____
   I shared my hurt with _____

He or she responded by_____

This week I was also sad about or hurt over _____
I shared my hurt with _____

He or she responded by _____

3.   Read Chapter 5 and complete the fill-in-the-blank sections.

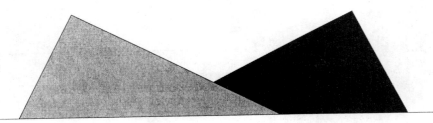

Chapter Summary

1. It is very important that we learn how to deal with hurt because it is the foundational painful emotion that can spawn other painful emotions.
2. Regardless of the source, form, or size of a hurt, the only proper response is comfort.
3. Jesus suffered all dimensions of hurt, so he is able to understand our pain.
4. Hurt can lead to anger, fear, and condemnation.
5. When we are hurting, we should share our hurt with a journeymate and receive comfort.
6. When someone else is hurting, the only proper initial response is to comfort him.
7. Often, a hurt is so deep and significant, the person who is hurt needs to be continually comforted.

Freedom from Anger

> Anyone can become angry – that is easy. But to be angry with the right person, to the right degree, at the right time, for the right purpose, and in the right way – that is not easy.
>
> Aristotle *(The Nicomachean Ethics)*

Let's begin our study of anger with a true/false test. (Circle your answers.)

1. True - False - I should never allow myself to be angry.
2. True - False - Anger can become sin.
3. True - False - I often get angry, and that's okay.
4. True - False - The more godly I become, the less often I'll become angry.
5. True - False - Redheads have a genetic predisposition toward anger.
6. True - False - When I'm angry, it's okay to spew on just anyone.

Now let's discuss each statement.

Statement # 1 - I should never allow myself to be angry. [False]

First of all, it's impossible never to become angry. With an extreme amount of self-control, we may get to where we don't *express* our anger (at least not overtly), but it's impossible never to get angry, and it's actually not good to try to suppress anger.

Testimony about misunderstanding anger

My father was an angry man. It seemed as if his anger was always simmering under the surface and periodically it would erupt. And it wasn't very pretty—cursing, objects hitting the wall. Growing up in this environment, I suffered a lot of emotional abuse. I began to think that anger was evil. I thought it was wrong in any form or fashion. So I became "Mr. Cool." I was determined that nothing would make me angry. Of course, I did get angry. I just didn't admit it or allow myself to express it.

This wrong perception of anger took a real toll on my marriage. My wife had a wholesome perspective on anger. When she was upset she expressed it, but I wouldn't accept that because I thought all anger was sin. I finally realized that there is nothing wrong with being angry if we properly deal with it. It took me a while to resolve all the pent-up anger that I had stuffed through the years, and I had to learn a new discipline relative to dealing with current anger. I also had to apologize to my wife for squelching her emotions through the years.

It's important to understand that anger is not sin. The fact that God gets angry (Numbers 11:1, 10) and Jesus was angry (Mark 3:5) forever settles this issue. Anger is a natural reaction to being hurt or offended. Anger is like a smoke detector: the sound a smoke detector makes may be annoying, but it alerts you to the fact that the air space has been violated. In like manner, anger can serve as a warning system.

Statement # 2 - Anger can become sin. [True]

Ephesians 4:26 says, "In your anger do not sin," so although anger is not initially sinful, it can become sin if it is not properly expressed and dealt with.

Unresolved anger can also digress to more serious stages. Unresolved anger becomes like a malignant cancer; if we don't properly deal with it, it can mutate into bitterness and hatred.

Statement # 3 - I often get angry, and that's okay. [False]

At first, this is going to seem a little contradictory because we've just said that it's okay to get angry. But we do have to deal with these Scriptures:

- "Everyone should be...slow to become angry" (James 1:19).
- "Love is not easily angered" (1 Corinthians 13:5).
- "The Lord is slow to anger, abounding in love" (Psalm 103:8).

Although it *is* acceptable to get angry, it should not be the norm. Anger should be the exception, not the rule.

For instance, Jesus occasionally became angry and he did express it, but he was also "slow to anger." His patience and compassion overrode any temptation to be quick-tempered and impatient. He was not an angry person.

In order to minimize feelings of anger, it often helps to learn to differentiate between major and minor issues and learn not to overreact to minor ones. There's a difference between getting angry over minor issues that are just a part of day-to-day living (you had a flat tire) and getting angry over a major issue (someone made fun of you). To the extent that we allow God to develop gentleness and patience in our lives, much of the anger caused by being frustrated or inconvenienced will subside.

Which of the following situations are probably just cause for getting angry? [Put an [x] by the ones you choose.]

_____The supermarket is out of your favorite brand of toilet paper.
_____Your two-year-old spills his milk on the table.
_____Your spouse forgets your birthday.
_____Your plane is delayed due to mechanical difficulties.
_____A business associate steals your big sale.
_____Your college alma mater loses its homecoming game.
_____Your teenage son disobeys you by driving the car on the weekend
      when you are out of town. He has a wreck.
_____Your neighbor promised to water your vegetable garden while you
      were gone on vacation, but he forgot and your plants died.
_____A robber breaks into your house and vandalizes your personal
      belongings.
_____You're calling someone and you're put on hold for five minutes.

On a scale from 1-10, are you "quick" or "slow" to get angry? [Put an [x] on the line.]

1..5...10
Slow   Quick

Why is this?

_____

_____

_____

Statement # 4 - The more godly I become, the less often I'll become angry. [Could be true, could be false]

As mentioned above, the more we allow God to perfect gentleness and patience in our lives, the less we'll be upset about petty matters. But spiritual maturity will not shield us from being hurt and having feelings of anger. Although a critical dimension of spiritual maturity involves learning how to deal properly with anger, no depth of spirituality will ever eliminate it. Again, God feels and expresses anger, so no level of spiritual maturity will eliminate anger.

Statement # 5 - Redheads have a genetic predisposition toward anger. (Let's not even go there.)

There is no such thing as a biological inclination toward anger, regardless of whether or not you are Irish, have red hair, or both. It is true that expressions of anger can be a learned behavior (if you grew up around a lot of shouting, you may be prone to shout yourself), but it's purely behavioral, not biological.

Statement # 6 - When I'm angry, it's okay to spew on just anyone. [False]

When we're angry it's important that we not arbitrarily take it out on whoever happens to be around us at the time. Ironically and painfully, the recipients of our anger are often those closest to us.

For instance, Larry had a rough day at the office, but he "bit his tongue" because he didn't want to make matters worse. On the way home he got a speeding ticket. In the first 30 minutes after coming home he:

- scolds his son because he forgot to take out the trash,
- ignores his daughter's obvious plea for attention, and
- speaks harsh words to his wife for no apparent reason.

What's wrong with this scenario?

Larry is taking out his anger on people who had nothing to do with what upset him. This is unfair, immature, and wrong.

Which of the six true-false statements was the most intriguing to you? Why?

_____

_____

Dealing with anger

Here are some suggestions on how to deal with anger:

1. Realize that anger comes from hurt.

In the last chapter, we discussed the fact that hurt can lead to anger (page 40). This is important to remember because to deal properly with anger we must also deal with the hurt beneath the anger.

When we understand that anger comes from hurt, we'll have keen insight into how to *respond* to an angry person. How do you respond to someone who blasts you with angry statements? Proverbs 15:1 says, "A gentle answer turns away wrath, but a harsh word stirs up anger." Realizing that beneath anger is hurt, what would a "gentle answer" sound like? A gentle answer is comprised of comforting words—words that address the person's hurt instead of his anger, because (as we learned in the last chapter) comfort ministers to hurt. What would "harsh words" be? Words that address the person's anger.

For instance, if someone spews, "I'm so sick and tired of this situation. Things better change around here or there will be hell to pay," a harsh word might be, "Oh grow up. You're always venting your spleen. Here's a quarter. Go call someone who cares." This response would surely "stir up anger." But a gentle answer, one that addresses hurt, might sound like this: "I can tell you're really upset. If you'd like to talk, I would be willing to listen. I care for you and certainly don't want you to be frustrated."

This response doesn't mean we ever have to "eat crow." A gentle answer is not an invitation to be abused. When someone consistently spews on us, we should confront him or her about it, but as a general principle, we should focus on an angry person's hurt instead of his anger.

2. Seek to understand what happened and why it happened.

First, seek to understand *what* happened. Get all the details. We may be angry about a situation for which we have partial or inaccurate information. In this case, simply getting all the facts can often help allay anger.

- *I'm angry because my friend stood me up for lunch.* (Maybe you went to the wrong restaurant.)
- *I'm angry because my co-worker got a new computer and I didn't.* (That may be true, but perhaps you're getting a promotion to a new position that comes with a new office complete with a new computer.)
- *I'm upset at my daughter's teacher because she isn't going to let her go on the field trip this Saturday.* (Perhaps your daughter is behind in her schoolwork or perhaps she has become a nuisance in the classroom.)

Proverbs 18:17 says, "The first to present his case seems right, till another comes forward and questions him," which simply means that there are usually two sides to every story, which further underscores the importance of getting all the facts. We may be angry because we've heard only one perspective. Upon hearing the other side of the story, we may realize our anger is unfounded.

Second, try to understand *why* something happened because, while it won't heal the hurt, it may help to relieve angry feelings.

- *I realize now that the reason my father never gave me any affection was because he never got any from his father.*

- *I realize now that the reason my parents would not allow me to spend time with certain friends is because they would have been a bad influence on me.*

In Leviticus 10, we read that Moses became very angry with Eleazar and Ithamar (Aaron's sons) because of the way they had handled a sin offering. What did he do? He talked to Aaron and got the facts, and "When Moses heard this, he was satisfied."

3. Properly express your anger to those involved in the situation as well as to someone who is uninvolved.

Properly express your anger to those involved in the situation because it may have these positive effects:

a. *Help you gain more understanding into what happened.* As mentioned above, getting the facts is important.

b. *Require those involved to give an account of their actions.* Matthew 18:15 says, "If your brother sins against you, go and show him his fault." If someone sins against you, he needs to know it; otherwise, your silence may cause him to think that what he did was okay, or he may think he "got away with it" which he may interpret as license to do it again. But when we confront those who have hurt us, we hold them responsible for their actions.

c. *Help develop sensitivity in those involved.* Perhaps what happened to you was not the result of sin (someone didn't technically wrong you), but perhaps the negative impact could have been minimized if handled more sensitively. *[I got upset yesterday when you told the kids about our vacation without my being there. I wanted to be there to see their reaction.* (Because you shared your hurt and anger, your spouse will probably think twice before he does something like this again.)] Proverbs 27:17 says, "As iron sharpens iron, so one man sharpens another," and this sharpening can take place as the truth is shared in love.

At times it is also helpful to share your feelings of hurt and anger with someone who was *not* involved in the situation because he may be able to help in these ways:

a. Offer an objective perspective on what happened. "*Sweetheart, I think you're misreading this situation,*" or "*You have every right to be angry.*")

b. Help give you understanding. "*The reason Cindy is treating you like that is because she's jealous of you.*"

c. Remove your aloneness. It's never good to keep strong emotions (hurt, anger, fear) to ourselves. We will feel blessed just by sharing our feelings with someone who will listen and care for us.

d. Comfort you. Ultimately, your hurt needs to be comforted. The people who were involved in the hurtful situation may or may not offer comfort. If they do not, you can receive the needed comfort from someone who wasn't even a part of the situation.

There are several cautions about sharing your hurt and anger with others:

a. Don't share just to find someone who will agree with you and take up your offense. You're not looking for someone simply to endorse your anger and/or justify your bad attitude.

b. It's best not to share with more than one or two people. If you share with a large group you'll probably digress into slander, rumors, gossip, and quarreling (2 Corinthians 12:20).

57

c. Don't share indiscriminately. Throughout this study we are encouraging you to develop a deep relationship with a journeymate. A deep mutual trust and a deep knowing of one another will provide a safe environment in which you can share the deep issues of your life. Jesus was discreet about what and to whom he shared, "But Jesus would not entrust himself to them, for he knew all men" (John 2:24).

Improper ways to express anger

When we're angry we're often tempted to deal with our anger in two improper ways: stuff it or spew it; or, put another way: hide it or hurl it. These are two extremes, two ruts on either side of the road.

Stuffers (hiders) have difficulty admitting that they're angry and have an even harder time expressing their anger. They tend to minimize their hurts and are reluctant to share.

Why do stuffers stuff? There are many possible reasons:

- They think anger is sin.
- They are uncomfortable with confrontation.
- They grew up around family members who stuffed their anger, so they've learned the same behavior.
- They grew up around family members who spewed their anger and, having been the recipient of that pain, they are doing just the opposite.
- Feelings of low self-worth make them feel as if they're not worthy of being heard.
- Fear inhibits their willingness to express anger.

Spewers (hurlers) are just the opposite. When they're upset, they let you know it, and it's usually not pretty. Why do spewers spew? There are many possible reasons:

- They don't know how to express their anger properly.
- They grew up around family members who spewed their anger, so they've learned the same behavior.
- Personal insecurities cause them to want to intimidate others.

Are you a stuffer or a spewer? Why?

_____

_____

_____

The best way to express anger is to share your hurt, not your anger. This requires discovering the hurt under the anger. For instance, if your business associate steals your big sale, instead of getting angry and kicking the dog or yelling at your children (spewing your anger), share your hurt with a journeymate: "Today my co-worker took advantage of me. I felt betrayed, duped, and belittled."

Even when we properly express anger, it usually takes a measure of self-control to keep from overreacting. That's why the Proverb says, "A fool gives full vent to his anger, but a wise man keeps himself under control" (Proverbs 29:11).

Avoid these *improper* ways to express anger:

1. Take it out on someone who didn't have anything to do with hurting you.

2. Become passive –aggressive. (*I'm going to get back at you in very subtle ways: I'll be late when you want to be on time; I'll neglect meeting your needs; I'll do what I know irritates you.*)
3. Verbally abuse people by saying hurtful things (for instance, attacking someone's character because he or she may have made a mistake).
4. Become violent - engage in physical violence (striking someone, throwing objects).

It's important to teach children how to express their anger verbally in a proper way. If not, they may stuff their anger, which is unhealthy, or they may vent their anger by coloring on the wall, hitting the dog, or other "acting out" situations. We are often all too quick to try to correct their behavior, *"Don't do that"* without first teaching them how to verbalize their anger verbally.

Ephesians 4:15 - The key to expressing anger properly

"Speak the truth in love" (Ephesians 4:15).

This one, simple phrase from Scripture provides a practical approach to expressing anger properly. It has three major parts:

1. *Speak.* When we're angry we need to express it. There's nothing spiritual about swallowing hard and "taking it."

2. **Speak the *truth*.** When we speak, we must be careful to speak only the truth. Whereas most of us wouldn't tell a bold–faced–lie, we may be tempted to *distort* the facts, *exaggerate* the facts, make *assumptions* (it has been said that assumption is the lowest form of knowledge), or only speak *part of the truth* (naturally, that part which substantiates our position). Instead, we must share only the truth and all of the truth. This may necessitate *pursuing* the truth—making some phone calls or getting some other opinions. Sometimes we may be upset over something because we're misinformed. Often, just talking out a situation—getting the facts—will dissolve our anger. So part of speaking the truth involves hearing all sides of the story before you speak.

3. **Speak the truth *in love*.** Some people think that, "armed with the truth," they have a "007 license to kill"; they can express their anger any way they want, even if it hurts their offender. Not so. We must share the truth *in love*. Sharing the truth in love involves being sensitive to *when* you share (Ephesians 4:29 defines unwholesome words as words spoken in an untimely manner), *how* you share (your tone of voice), and even your body language (a gentle, non-intimidating posture is best).

When speaking the truth in love,
- Get to the point quickly.
- Stick to the issue at hand.
- Be confidential in what you say. Just because what you share is "truth" doesn't give you permission to share with those not directly involved in the situation.

Which of these three aspects are you most like to violate? Why?

Some helpful hints on how to "speak the truth in love"

[Before reading this next section, make a list of your close relationships. Include family members, friends, co-workers, etc.]

---

1. Be approachable.

To keep relationships healthy, we need to be approachable; let those around you know that if you offend them, you want them to approach you and talk it out. Give them permission to share the truth in love with you: "When I do something that hurts you, or if you misunderstand something I do or say, please come to me and share the truth in love. I promise to receive you and listen to what you have to say."

To be approachable doesn't mean you must change your mind or position to concur with whoever is approaching you. Even after someone speaks the truth to you in love, you may want to stick to your conviction or even defend yourself. Being approachable simply means that people should always feel the freedom to come and talk to you.

Becoming approachable has nothing to do with lines of authority. We never want to convey the message, "I'm the father, and you're the child. Don't ever confront me with an issue" or, "I'm the boss, you're my employee. You don't have the right to approach me, even if I'm wrong."

In an effort to become more approachable, visit with everyone you listed above and give them permission to speak to you whenever they want.

2. Define what "in love" means for each significant person in your life so that when you need to *share the truth*, you'll know the proper time, place, and approach. In other words, everyone has his own personal criteria as to what "in love" means. Imagine each person on your list giving his or her own specific guidelines, such as these:

- Not as soon as I get home from work.
- Not in front of the kids.
- Don't raise your voice at me.
- Not in front of other people.
- Don't condemn me; don't attack who I am.
- Allow me to share my side of the story.
- Not when I'm tired.
- Not on Sundays, particularly not before worship services.
- Try to understand what I'm saying, even if it doesn't come out in a logical way.

Refer again to the above list. In time, ask each person what "in love" means to him or her. And mention that the next time you need to "share the truth in love," you'll try to abide by his or her personal guidelines.

How would you define what "in love" means to you?

In time, share your personal preferences with the individuals listed above.

Forgiving our offender

The first step in dealing with our anger is to speak the truth in love. The second is to forgive the person who has offended us.

When we are angry about having been hurt, there are two possible causes, and it's important to differentiate between the two:

a. I was hurt by someone's sin; I was wronged.
- *My spouse lied to me.*
- *My father emotionally abused me.*
- *My spouse was unfaithful to me.*
- *My friend talked poorly about me behind my back.*
- *My mother verbally abused me.*

b. My hurt was due to circumstances, not someone's sin.
- *I was frustrated and upset because my car stalled in rush-hour traffic.*
- *My friend and I had a major misunderstanding; it turns out that neither of us was "wrong" but it hurt nevertheless.*
- *My flight was canceled because of bad weather.*

When we are hurt by someone's sin (we are wronged), a vital aspect of releasing our anger is to *forgive our offender*. But if our hurt was caused by circumstances, forgiveness is not always necessary or even appropriate. For instance, if you're frustrated and upset that your car stalled in rush-hour traffic, there's really nothing or no one to forgive in this situation.

But if we are angry because we have been wronged, we must forgive.

Here are some guidelines on forgiveness.

1. Forgiveness is a choice, a function of our will.

When we are offended, we must *choose* to forgive because we will seldom *feel* like forgiving. The truth is, we seldom feel like forgiving those who have hurt us. Ephesians 4:31 says, "Get rid of all bitterness, rage, and anger." The Greek word for "get rid of" is "airo" which means to "carry off or take away." When we forgive someone, we "let go of" the offense. It is an act of our will.

2. Forgiveness is a matter of stewardship.

We are to forgive others because we have been forgiven. Colossians 3:13 says, "Forgive as the Lord forgave you." We are often reluctant to forgive because our offender doesn't deserve being forgiven. The truth is, *no one* deserves to be forgiven; it is one of the manifold graces of God. When we forgive others, we are simply sharing with them some of what God has already given us. If we have difficulty forgiving others, it may be because we have not yet received God's forgiveness, or perhaps we have forgotten about his gift to us.

Testimony about sharing God's gift of forgiveness

I recently counseled a couple whose marriage had been wounded by the husband's infidelity. After a few sessions he became genuinely remorseful about his sin, got on his knees in front of his wife, and with tears in his eyes, confessed his sin and asked for her forgiveness. I was surprised by her answer. She said, "No." The husband looked up at me, as if to ask, "What do I do now?" I really didn't know what to tell him. We quickly ended that session.

During the following week, the Lord spoke to my heart through Colossians 3:13 (Forgive one another, as you have been forgiven). It occurred to me that perhaps the wife was having a hard time forgiving because she had never received God's forgiveness herself; therefore, she had nothing to offer.

The following week I met with the couple and in a very simple way, I presented the gospel message and asked each of them if they had ever asked Christ to be their Savior and Lord. He had; she had not. I then asked her if she would like to receive God's gift of eternal life. She said she would. We prayed together in my office that day, and God's amazing grace once again escorted a human soul from the domain of darkness into his marvelous light.

I then told her this story from Matthew 18, a story that Jesus told when teaching on forgiveness.

"There once was a servant who owed his king ten thousand talents of gold. In today's currency that's several million dollars. He could not pay so the king had him thrown into prison. But the servant appealed to the king and the king was merciful. Not only did he release the man from prison, but he also forgave his debt.

The same servant had a slave who owed him a hundred denarii (a few dollars in today's currency). The servant demanded the slave to pay the debt. When he could not, the servant ignored his plea for mercy and had him thrown into prison.

When the king heard about this, he was furious. He called the servant in and said, 'You wicked servant, I canceled all your debt because you begged me to. Shouldn't you have had mercy on your fellow servant just as I had on you?' The king then turned him over to the jailers until he should pay back all he owed." The chapter ends with Jesus saying, "This is how my heavenly Father will treat each of you unless you forgive your brother from your heart."

I explained to the wife that in this story the King represents God, the servant represents you and me, and the slave represents those who "owe" us, that is, those who have offended us. The lesson is obvious; because of our sin, we owe an enormous debt to God that is impossible to pay. We deserve a prison sentence. But God forgives us; he cancels our debt. People who have offended us are technically in our debt, but since we have received forgiveness from God, we are free to (and must) cancel the debt they owe us.

I then appealed to her by saying, "Having now received forgiveness from God, would you be willing to share some of it with your husband?" She did.

3. We should forgive whether or not our offender asks our forgiveness.

We're often asked, "If someone has offended me, shouldn't I wait until he asks my forgiveness before I forgive him?"

The testimony of Jesus will answer this question.

While on the cross he prayed, "Father, forgive them for they don't know what they're doing" (Luke 23:34). Obviously, at this point, the masses were not asking for forgiveness, but Jesus forgave them nevertheless. Forgiveness is not based on whether our offender deserves our forgiveness or whether or not he asks for it. We are to forgive because we have been forgiven; it's a matter of stewardship. Since it is forgiveness that removes anger from our cup, if we refuse to forgive someone unless he asks our forgiveness, and he never asks, we will suffer the consequences of having anger remain in our cup.

Furthermore, what if our offender is deceased, in which case a confession from him is impossible? For instance, what if you're seriously injured in a car wreck caused by a drunken driver and the intoxicated driver is killed in the accident? If you say, "I'm not going to forgive until my offender confesses" you'll never be released from anger.

Testimony regarding forgiving our offenders whether or not they ask our forgiveness

Years ago, a man really hurt my wife and me very deeply. He was not a Christian, so we had difficulty communicating to him about this issue. The problem dragged on for years. Three years later, he showed up at our house one evening and asked to come in. We were really surprised when he confessed that what he had done to us years earlier was wrong. He asked our forgiveness. We were deeply touched. We replied, "Thank you so much for coming tonight. We appreciate what you have said, and we want you to know that we forgave you three years ago when the incident first happened. Yes, you are forgiven."

1. Had the couple not forgiven their offender years earlier, what might they have carried in their emotional cups through the years?

2. When the man came to their house and confessed, what did he empty out of his emotional cup?

4. We should not make our forgiveness conditional.

When God forgave us, he did so with "no strings attached." We are to do likewise. In other words, we shouldn't say,

- *I'll forgive you if you promise to never do it again.*
- *I'll forgive you if you'll clean the house.*
- *I'll forgive you but I'm going to sulk for days.*
- *I'll forgive you but only after I tell everyone what you did.*
- *I'll forgive you this time but not if you do it again.*

Genuine forgiveness never involves an "if" or "but."

5. It *is* acceptable to share with our offender how deeply we were hurt by what happened.

As we mentioned above, we should never put conditions on our forgiveness, but it is appropriate, when possible, to share with our offender how deeply he hurt us.

Testimony about sharing your hurt with your offender

My husband hurt me deeply when he violated our marriage by having an affair. For months after I found out, he didn't even want to talk about it. But one evening, after we had finished dinner, he walked up to me while I was cleaning the kitchen and said, "Sweetheart, I realize that my being unfaithful to you was wrong; would you forgive me?"

I was really shocked and confused. On the one hand, I appreciated the fact that he was confessing, but on the other hand, I felt that if I said "yes," he'd just walk off and that would be the end of it. I desperately needed to talk this out.

So I replied, "Honey, I appreciate the fact that you've come to me and confessed. It would mean a lot to me if we could sit down tonight and talk. I really need to tell you how much this has hurt me."

That evening we spent several hours talking. I was able to share with him the depth of my pain, how I had felt betrayed, humiliated, hurt, and disappointed. He listened intently, and the more I shared, the more sorrowful he felt over hurting me. I really believe God brought a depth of understanding to my husband during that time that was lacking before. When I finished expressing my hurt, I said, "I forgive you."

As I reflect on that incident, I realize that I was to forgive him even if we didn't get to talk it out. Actually, I was to forgive him even if he didn't ask for my forgiveness, but being able to share how I was feeling brought great healing to my life and our relationship.

6. If someone genuinely forgives someone else but continues to be angry over the offense (he can't seem to "get over it"), we should look deeper and minister to the hurt that may be keeping his anger "alive."

We were recently asked, "As an act of my will, I have forgiven a person who hurt me deeply, but I just can't forget it nor do I seem to be able to 'get over it.' I thought we were supposed to forgive and forget—but how?"

Yes, we are to forgive, but sometimes it is hard, if not impossible, to forget. You can't "erase" the memory of a painful event as you can delete a file in your computer. However, there's probably another factor to consider here which may be keeping the offense alive and debilitating.

Earlier in this chapter we talked about the fact that anger is a by-product of hurt; when we have been hurt we get angry. So there are really two emotions that must be dealt with: anger and hurt. Anger can often be released through forgiveness, but hurt must be mourned and comforted. Oftentimes, we may properly deal with our anger through forgiveness, but we neglect dealing with the hurt. The unresolved hurt continues to affect us adversely and may keep the anger "alive."

Whenever you struggle over being angry about a situation you thought you had properly dealt with, tell your journeymate about the hurt that caused the anger and receive comfort. Although the actual memory of the offense may never go away, you'll experience freedom if the hurt that caused it is comforted.

On a scale from 1-10, are you "quick" or "slow" to forgive?

1..5..10
Slow   Quick

Why are you at this level?

_____

_____

"To forgive is to set the captive free; only to discover that all along, the captive was me."

Discussion Questions (Discuss these issues in your group or with your journeymate.)

1. What was the most interesting concept presented in this chapter?
2. How are these vices related to anger: quick temper, impatience, critical spirit?
3. Each person respond to this question: "When you feel yourself getting angry, do you try to get all the facts?"
4. Read Luke 23:34. What can we learn from Jesus' statement of forgiveness?
5. Each person tell how you defined "in love" for yourself (refer to page 60).
6. What should we do when we are angry at God?
7. If time allows, process the *Freedom from Anger Learning Activity* that is located in the Facilitator's Guide.

Journeymate time (Discuss these issues with your journeymate.)

1. Share with your journeymate the results of your homework from last week.
2. Share with your journeymate your responses to the fill-in-the-blank sections for this week's lesson.
3. When was the last time you got angry? Was the situation worth getting angry over? How did you deal with the situation? What was the result?
4. Do you have difficulty forgiving others? If so, why?
5. Who has hurt you the most in life? Have you forgiven this person?
6. As you consider the emotional cup illustration, what anger might be in your cup as a result of past situations? Visit with your journeymate about possibly needing to forgive your offenders.
7. What has been your greatest experience of receiving God's forgiveness?

Homework

1. Meet with your journeymate and reconsider the sixth question under the Journeymate section. Devote as much time as necessary to emptying your cup of all anger.
2. This week, if you get angry, try to get all the facts and share your hurt with your journeymate. If you are angry because someone sinned against you, share the truth in love with your offender, try to understand why your offender did what he did, and forgive your offender.

Record your experiences here:

I got angry because

_____

I sought to get all the facts by

_____

If someone sinned against you, write out your forgiveness. "Father, I forgive

_____

_____

If you were angry because someone offended you, write out whether or not you were able to share the truth in love and, if you did, record what happened.

_____

_____

Write out why your offender might have done what he or she did.

_____

3. Read Chapter 6 and complete the fill-in-the-blank sections.

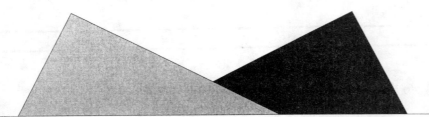

Chapter Summary

1. Anger is a legitimate emotion. It is a normal response to having been hurt. However, anger should be expressed properly and resolved quickly.

2. As a part of resolving anger, it is important to try to discover *what* happened and *why* it happened.

3. Relative to expressing anger, there are two extremes to avoid; spewing and stuffing.

4. The key to expressing anger properly is Ephesians 4:15 – "Speak the truth in love."

5. If someone has sinned against us, we must forgive him.

Freedom from Fear

A little boy had a part in the school play that read, "It is I, be not afraid."
He came out on stage and said, "It's me and I'm scared."

- For Angela, flying is a nerve-wracking experience. Recently, her friend told her that a person is more likely to be killed driving to the airport than flying on a commercial jet, but she's still afraid. Facts and statistics don't ease the anxiety Angela feels when a jet she's flying in starts rumbling down the runway. When in the air, every time the plane encounters turbulence, her heart races.

  Angela + flying = fear.

- Randy feels like a round peg trying to fit into a square hole. He's enrolled in a month-long summer study course for high school seniors, and he's been away from home for three weeks. It's his first time away from his family and his first time on a college campus. He knows he's in a safe environment; but at times, particularly at night, fear comes upon him like a dark cloud. Randy can't really identify *what* he's afraid of, but fear has a vise-grip on his soul.

- Elizabeth was twelve years old when her parents divorced. She watched with horror and incredulity as one of the most important persons in her life, her father, packed up his personal belongings and walked out the front door. She later discovered that another woman was involved in the breakup. Twelve years later Elizabeth and her husband Bob have just celebrated their first anniversary. Except for a few misunderstandings and "adjustment sessions," their first year of marriage has gone remarkably well except for one aspect. Elizabeth is inordinately jealous; she worries about Bob's fidelity. Bob has never done anything to justify her suspicions—he's a "one-woman man"—but she still struggles every time he leaves for a business trip or when he talks with another woman. Underneath her jealousy is fear.

Fear is an emotion common to humanity. Even the Apostle Paul testified to his struggle with fear: "For when we came into Macedonia...we were harassed at every turn...conflicts on the outside, fears within" (2 Corinthians 7:6); and he shared with the Corinthian church that, "I came to you in weakness and fear and with much trembling" (1 Corinthians 2:3).

Initial feelings of fear can be normal and even healthy. But fear, if left unresolved, can become detrimental.

It's important to understand that emotional fear is not sin, so it doesn't need to be confessed as such. For instance, when the angel Gabriel appeared to Mary, the mother of

Jesus, and said, "Do not be afraid, Mary, you have found favor with God," he was not chiding her—"stop being afraid, that's wrong"—he was simply trying to comfort her. But God doesn't want us to live with a constant burden of fear.

Types of Fear

The fear of the Lord

There is a "holy fear" which is always healthy and desirable. The Bible calls it the "fear of the Lord." A synonym would be reverence. We should have an awe and respect for the sovereignty and holiness of God. King David described this type of fear as clean and pure (Psalm 19:9), and Solomon said it is the beginning of wisdom (Proverbs 1:7).

Fear of identifiable danger

A normal sense of fear may grip us when we are faced with the threat of danger. If a German shepherd breaks its leash and is running full speed to attack you, there's good reason to be afraid. Or if you're awakened at night by strange noises in your house, anxiety is appropriate because God has wired us to respond to potentially dangerous situations. This type of fear is prompted by obvious signs of danger, and it usually diminishes once the source of danger is resolved. This "response mechanism" aspect of fear is healthy because it can help us avoid dangerous situations and properly respond to them.

Lingering anxiety and worry

The most debilitating type of fear is a lingering sense of apprehension and dread, a fear that produces anxiety and troubles the soul. This fear can plague us even when there is no apparent danger—it is often even irrational. It tenaciously grips the soul and won't let go. It can impede our ability to think and act.

In this chapter we'll discuss this third type of fear.

Symptoms of fear

Fear can cause physical symptoms such as increased heart rate, high blood pressure, chest pain, shortness of breath, fatigue, lightheadedness, panic attacks, or intense headaches.

Fear can also impact our behavior toward others. For instance, we may become controlling, attempting to control people, our environment, agendas, etc. The reasoning is, "I'm fearful of the future, but if I can control everything and everyone around me, I'll be in control so I can make sure things work out favorably for me."

Fear can also cause us to be intolerant and critical of others. Fear and insecurity may cause us to resist people who are different from us and avoid situations that are unpredictable. We'll stay well within our comfort zone and remain intimidated by, and therefore intolerant of, anyone who is different.

Unresolved fear can escalate into phobias. We may become intensely afraid of the dark, heights, enclosed areas, the weather, flying, and other things.

Sources of fear

1. Past hurt

As mentioned in Chapter 4, hurt is a root emotion which can yield other painful emotions. Unresolved hurt from the past can lead to present fear.

- I suffered through a very hurtful divorce. Now I'm afraid to get close to anyone.
- I was in a bad car accident when I was young. Now I'm afraid to drive.
- Mom died of cancer when she was 32 years old. Now I'm afraid I'll get ill.

To the extent that fear is based on hurt, the hurt must be properly dealt with before the fear will subside. Refer again to Chapter 4 to learn how to deal properly with the underlying hurt that may be causing and sustaining fear in your life.

Testimony about how hurt can lead to fear.

When I was eight years old, my sister and I were alone in the house when a tornado struck. We were frightened and didn't know what to do. We cowered under the kitchen table and moments later part of the roof was ripped off. Even after the storm blew over we were alone for about 30 minutes till Mom and Dad came home. It was a horrible experience.

Ever since then, I've been afraid of storms. Whenever the clouds get dark and the wind picks up, I get nervous and anxious.

2. Lies from Satan and our own self-talk

Satan is called the father of lies (John 8:44), which implies that he tells a lot of them and that he's good at it. Quite often, his lies are intended to make us fearful.

- We'll read an article in the newspaper about teenage drug abuse and he'll suggest, "Your kid will become part of the drug culture."
- We'll wake up in the middle of the night and he'll tell us, "Your boss is really disappointed in you."
- A friend will share with us the pain of his divorce and he'll suggest the thought, "Your marriage is going to end in divorce, too."
- We'll listen to a documentary on colon cancer and Satan will tell us, "You're a likely candidate."

But we can't always blame the devil for errant thoughts. Lies are often self-inflicted. Our minds will wander aimlessly, inadvertently attach to a random thought, embrace it, embellish it, believe it—and then we're trapped.

Later in this chapter we'll discuss how truth can dispel lies.

Testimony about how lies can cause us to be fearful

I have two small children. One of my biggest fears in life was that I would be a bad father. I lived with a constant sense of inadequacy and was always anxious about it.

One day I had the courage to share my fear with a group of men I meet with regularly. They were really surprised to hear of my fear because they all sensed that I was a loving, caring father. We explored the source of my fear. I couldn't identify any hurt from my past that would be fueling the fear. We finally realized that my fear was simply based on a lie from the enemy. Satan had planted a thought in my mind, "You'll never be a good father," and then my self-talk took over and escalated that single lie into a major issue.

The men ministered truth to me (I am indeed a loving, caring father), prayed for me, and they continue to reinforce the truth to me every time we meet.

3. The unusual and the unknown.

When an angel appeared to Mary the mother of Jesus, she was afraid, and understandably so. How would you feel if a supernatural, angelic being stood before you? Mary's fear was not based on past hurt or lies. She was afraid simply because something very unusual was happening.

Likewise, we may experience natural, even anticipated anxiety over certain events, particularly first-time events. For instance, how did you feel

- On your first day of elementary school?
- On your first day at a new job?
- During your first trip overseas?
- During your first semester at college?

Some may respond, "I felt great. New environments don't frighten me." But others may say, "I really got anxious when faced with a new situation."

Perhaps the disciples were feeling anxious about the unknown when Jesus announced that after three years of being together, he was going to leave them. Anxious thoughts no doubt raced through their hearts: "What are we going to do after Jesus leaves? Just fish and collect taxes again? What will we do if we get in a jam and Jesus isn't here to rescue us? What if the Pharisees ask us a question we can't answer?" Jesus, sensing their anxiety, said to them, "Do not let your hearts be troubled. Trust in God; trust also in me" (John 14:1).

What is the greatest fear you struggle with?

_____

_____

What is the source of this fear?

_____

_____

Dimensions of fear- Freedom from fear

As humans, we have a mind (we're able to think and reason), a will (we're able to make decisions), and emotions (we're able to feel). Fear impacts all three areas, and there is a distinct biblical solution to all three.

The **mental** dimension of fear is ministered to by **truth** (John 8:32).
The **emotional** dimension of fear is ministered to by **perfect love** (1 John 4:18).
The **volitional** dimension of fear is ministered to by **faith** (Luke 8:25).

Freedom from fear will usually involve all three antidotes, but the degree to which each element is needed is often determined by the *source* of fear.

The following percentages are estimations (you may have your own opinion about the relative importance that each aspect has), but they convey the need for all three antidotes—truth, love and faith—in dealing with fear.

Fear based on past hurt is -
Mental - 20%
Emotional - 60%
Volitional - 20%

Fear based on lies is -
Mental - 50%
Emotional - 30%
Volitional - 20%

Fear based on the unusual and the unknown is -
Mental - 20%
Emotional - 40%
Volitional - 40%

Let's discuss these three antidotes for fear.

1. Truth

John 8:32 says that truth will set us free. Particularly when our fear is based on lies, truth will help bring relief.

Let's revisit some of the lies that were listed earlier in the chapter and see how truth could give relief.

- We'll read an article in the newspaper about teenage drug abuse and Satan will suggest, "Your kid will someday become part of the drug culture."
  Truth - There is no correlation between reading an article on teenage drug abuse and your child's becoming a drug addict.

- We'll wake up in the middle of the night and Satan will tell us, "Your boss is really disappointed in you."
  Truth - Maybe your boss is disappointed, maybe not. Make an appointment with him and ask him. Then you'll know the truth.

- A friend will share with us the pain of his divorce and we'll have the thought, "Your marriage is going to end in divorce, too."
  Truth - Your friend's broken marriage is no predictor of the security of your marriage. Visit with your spouse and discuss the truth.

- We'll listen to a documentary on colon cancer and be impressed that, "You're a likely candidate."
  Truth - The best way to know the truth is to visit your doctor and have some tests run.

Think of a time when your fear was based upon a lie, and the fear was resolved by the truth. Write about it here.

2. Perfect love

1 John 4:18 teaches that "Perfect love drives out fear."

Throughout this book we have noted that when someone expresses an emotion and we respond with a "head" answer, it usually misses the mark. This is particularly true when someone is afraid. For instance, if a child is afraid of the dark and begins to cry, appealing to his rational mind probably won't help: "Johnny, don't be afraid of the dark, there's no such thing as monsters. And even if there were, they couldn't get past the alarm system." Don't expect Johnny to say, "Gee, Dad, that's good to know. Thanks for telling me. I'm fine now. You can go back to bed."

Or, if someone is anxious because he's staying on the 29th floor of a hotel and he's afraid of heights, try ministering to his fear by reading statistics from a structural engineer's report on how safe the building is. Sharing facts probably won't help.

Granted, sometimes our fear *is* based on facts—"My company is downsizing and I'm afraid I'll lose my job"—in which case our anxiety can be diminished or heightened by reasoning, "You're not going to lose your job" or "Your job *is* being eliminated." But often, because of the strong emotional dimension of fear, perfect love is the only thing that will bring relief.

What does perfect love look like, feel like, and sound like? When someone is fearful, is it sufficient just to say "I love you" and then assume the fear will subside? Probably not. Perfect love must be shared and experienced.

Listed below are some biblical ways in which we can express perfect love to those who are fearful. As we discuss each verse, we'll revisit Angela's, Randy's and Elizabeth's situations (mentioned at the beginning of this chapter) and show how perfect love can help minister to their fear.

Perfect love is expressed through our reassuring presence

"Do not fear...**for I am with you**" (Isaiah 41:10).

When someone is fearful, the worst thing that can happen is for her to be alone. It's important to remove her physical and emotional aloneness. In Isaiah 41:10, the Lord is ministering to our fears by assuring us of his presence.

Ministering to Angela's fear of flying might mean
- Sitting next to her on the plane, holding her hand.
- Talking to her and praying with her during take-off and landing.
- If you can't go with her, write her a reassuring, comforting note she can read after boarding the plane.

Randy's fear of being away from home might be allayed by
- Calling him several times a day.
- Writing him daily and sending an occasional "care package."
- Planning a surprise visit. Just 24 hours with family and friends can bring great relief.
- Telling him that you will fast specifically for him one day a week. On that day he will feel a unique spiritual closeness with you.

The "aloneness" of Elizabeth's hurt, caused by her father's desertion, might be removed by
- Allowing her to share the hurt and pain she experienced, entering into her pain, and then comforting her.
- Helping her to visit with her mother and father to facilitate a healing between her and them.

Have you ever had your fears lovingly "cast out" by someone's loving and caring presence? Write about it here.

Perfect love is expressed through our caring involvement

"Fear not, **I have redeemed you**" (Isaiah 43:1).

When people are fearful, they need to know that you love and care for them, and that you'll be available to meet their needs. By saying "I have redeemed you," the Lord conveys to us that he loves and cares for us and that he has met, and always will meet, the most important needs in our lives.

For Angela, this might mean
- Expressing words of love and comfort such as, "Angela, I love you and care for you. I want to be available for you when you need me."
- Lovingly meeting her needs for attention, approval, comfort, and encouragement.
- Refraining from criticizing and minimizing her fear of flying.
- When logistically possible, offering to drive her to her destination.

Ministering to Randy's need for love and caring involvement might include
- Expressing words of love and comfort like those shared with Angela.
- Reassuring him that loving relationships have not changed just because he's "out of sight." He's still a vital part of the family and greatly missed.
- Asking some of his friends to write and/or visit him.

<u>Elizabeth's fear could be ministered to by</u>
- Bob's reassuring her that he loves her and is committed to be understanding and supportive of her, even in the midst of her jealousy and fear.
- Bob's refraining from defending himself but concentrating on ministering to her needs.
- When Bob is out of town, he could frequently call Elizabeth and keep her apprised of where he is and what he's doing. Praying with her over the phone would be another strong reassurance.
- Realizing his wife's fear of marital infidelity, Bob should be committed to avoid every appearance of evil.

Perfect love is expressed through the promise of future love and care

"Do not let your hearts be troubled...**I am going to prepare a place for you**" (John 14:1-2).

While hurt and anger are related to the past, fear is future oriented. We're not fearful about what happened in the past (though we may be hurt and angry); we're fearful about what might happen in the future. Our fear may often be prompted by a past event (this is particularly true in Elizabeth's life), in which case the past has to be properly dealt with as the underlying pain is comforted through reassuring love. Regardless of what prompted the fear, fear always affects our perspective on the future.

Therefore, a meaningful way to minister to a person's fear is to provide reassurance about the future. In John 14, Jesus addressed his disciples' anxiety about his impending departure by assuring them that he was concerned for their future, he was preparing for their future, and he would be with them in the future: "I will come back and take you to be with me that you also may be where I am" (John 14:3).

<u>This message of comfort might be communicated to Angela by</u>
- Assuring her that your commitment to love and care for her is a permanent and unconditional commitment; you'll be there for her in the future.
- Reminding her that God has promised never to leave or forsake her (Hebrews 13:5), and that his plans for her are for good and not evil (Jeremiah 29:11).

<u>Randy's feelings of fear will subside as</u>
- His parents help him focus on the hope and joy of his coming home.
- He is reminded of his home, that he is missed, and that the family "isn't the same without him."
- His parents reassure him that God will be there as the God of all comfort and that he will work all this for Randy's ultimate good.

<u>Bob can minister to Elizabeth's fear by continually assuring her that</u>
- He's committed to their relationship for life and that he will always be available to meet her needs.
- He doesn't have "eyes" for any other woman and will always be morally faithful to her.
- He has deep spiritual convictions about marriage and family concerns.

Christians - Conduits of Perfect Love

Yes, perfect love is an antidote for fear, and only God's love is perfect. But how does God distribute his love? How does he get his perfect love in circulation so that we can experience his love?

One way is to receive his love directly, by spending time with the Lord in prayer and meditation and by reading his "love letter," the Bible.

Another way that God desires to distribute his love is through his body, the church—and that includes you!

3. Faith

In Mark 5, Jesus and his disciples are in a boat when a terrible storm threatens to swamp them. The disciples, fearing for their lives, cry out, "Teacher, don't you care if we drown?" After Jesus calms the storm, he says to them, "Why are you so afraid? Do you still have no faith?" In this instance, evidently it was faith that should have eliminated their fear.

Romans 10:17 says that "Faith comes from hearing the message, and the message is heard through the word of Christ." Simply stated, we are to put our faith in what God says.

In the story in Mark 5, what was the "word of Christ"? What had Jesus already spoken about the situation? Before getting into the boat, Jesus had told them, "Let's go over to the other side." The disciples should have realized that if Jesus said they were going to the other side, and were going to the other side! In this case, their faith in his word should have supplanted their fear.

Just as fear is future-oriented (we do not fear the past), faith is also future-oriented: "Now faith is being sure of what we hope for and certain of what we do not see" (Hebrews 11:1). That's why faith is an effective antidote for fear. Relative to the future, we choose to live by one or the other.

Many Scriptures reassure us of God's care for us in the future and assure us that we can place our faith in his word:

➤ "God has said, 'never will I leave you; never will I forsake you'" (Hebrews 13:5).
➤ "Do not be anxious about anything, but in everything, by prayer and petition, with thanksgiving, present your requests to God" (Philippians 4:6).
➤ "Therefore I tell you, do not worry about your life...your heavenly Father knows (what you need)… But seek first his kingdom and his righteousness, and all these things will be given to you as well" (Matthew 6:25,32,33).

As we look to the future, we can view it through the lens of fear or the lens of faith. Write down a fear you have that relates to the uncertainty of the future. (*I'm afraid of getting old; what if my health fails? Our society is becoming more and more godless; I'm afraid for the future of my children.*)

_____

_____

_____

Now meditate on the three Scripture verses written above and by faith receive God's promises.

Never struggle with fear *alone*.

In Genesis 2:18 God declared that "It is not good for the man to be alone." While there are many reasons *why* it's not good for man to be alone, perhaps the most compelling is that we should not, and at times cannot, deal with painful emotions alone. For instance, it hurts to hurt, but when we hurt alone, the pain is magnified. Likewise, fear is unpleasant in and of itself, but when we have to face our fears alone, our uneasiness is amplified.

That's why, throughout this study, we have encouraged you to establish a close relationship with a journeymate, someone with whom you can be open and honest and someone who will connect with you emotionally.

It's not uncommon for a person to keep her fears to herself for years—even for a lifetime. But God wants us to bear each other's burdens (Galatians 6:2), and that includes sharing and bearing the fears and anxieties with which we struggle.

Wouldn't it be profitable to share with someone who loves you, all the fears and anxieties with which you struggle? And to be able to do that on a regular basis?
This is God's design and will.

A small voice penetrated the stillness of the night, "Daddy, I'm scared!" The father responded, "Honey, don't be afraid, Daddy's right across the hall." After a brief pause, the little boy said, "I'm still scared," to which the father added, "You don't need to be afraid. God is with you. God loves you." After a longer pause, his son said, "Daddy, I'm still scared. I want someone with skin on!"

Discussion questions (Discuss these issues in your group or with your journeymate.)

1. What was the most interesting concept presented in this chapter?
2. God often chooses to distribute some of his perfect love through us. Share a time when God used you as a channel through which he displaced another person's fear. Share a time when God used someone else to minister to your fear.
3. When a child is afraid, what is the best way to minister to him? Will the same strategy work for an adult?
4. Why is faith an antidote for fear?

Journeymate time (Discuss these issues with your journeymate.)

1. Share with your journeymate the results of your homework from last week.
2. Share with your journeymate your responses to the fill-in-the-blank sections in this week's lesson.
3. As you consider the emotional cup illustration, share with your journeymate some of your fears. Are the fears
   - rooted in past hurts (*I'm afraid of storms because I was once in a tornado*)?
   - prompted by current stress (*I'm afraid my car will be repossessed because I've not been able to make my car payments*)?
   - built upon lies (*I'm afraid I'll never get married*)? or
   - based on the unusual or unknown (*I'm starting a new job next week and I don't know what to expect*)?

   Minister God's perfect love to each other by applying the biblical principles discussed in this chapter.

Homework (to be completed before the next meeting)

1. This week, consider those with whom you have a close relationship. Consider how you can be an instrument of God's love in their lives, helping to minister freedom from their fears. Record your experiences:

This week I noticed that _____ might have been struggling with fear. I ministered God's perfect love by _____.

This week I noticed that _____ might have been struggling with fear. I ministered God's perfect love by _____.

2. This week, if you become fearful or anxious, share your feelings with your journeymate.
   Record your experience here:

This week I felt anxious about _____.

I shared it with _____ and his or her response was _____

_____

I ended up feeling _____.

    3.   Read Chapter 7 and complete the fill-in-the-blank sections.

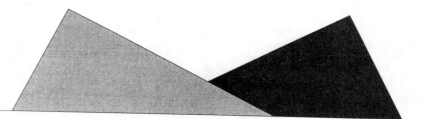

Chapter Summary

1. There are different types of fear: the fear of the Lord, fear of identifiable danger, and a lingering sense of anxiety and worry. In this chapter we focus on the last type (lingering sense of anxiety and worry).

2. There are three sources of fear: past hurt, lies, and the unusual and unknown.

3. There are three dimensions of fear (mental, emotional, and volitional) and three antidotes for fear (truth – John 8:32; perfect love – 1 John 4:18; and faith – Luke 8:25). Depending on the source and dimension of a particular fear, a combination of the three antidotes is needed to bring relief.

4. We should never try to deal with fear alone. Close, intimate relationships will help shield us from fearful thoughts and will also provide relief from them.

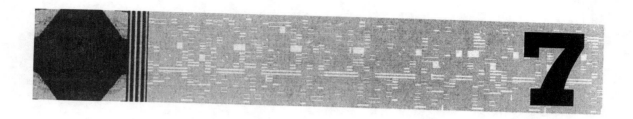

Freedom from Guilt

*"And forgive us our trash baskets as we forgive those
who put trash in our baskets."*
A four-year old

Feelings of guilt are the natural by-product of sin. When we do something wrong, we *should* feel guilty. Appropriate feelings of guilt are actually a sign of spiritual health. If we sin and *don't* feel guilt, something is wrong.

But God never intended for guilt to remain in our emotional cup. In this regard, guilt and anger are somewhat similar in that they both have a potentially positive, short-term effect (guilt tells us that we have hurt others; anger tells us that we have been hurt), but they will adversely affect us if not properly resolved.

Read 1 John 1:8, 10. According to these verses, why is it important to confess our sins to God and to maintain a clear conscience?

_____

_____

Testimony about the importance of feeling guilty when we have wronged someone

To be honest, until recently, I'm not sure that I have ever *felt* a lot of guilt. My conscience just never bothered me. The Bible says the Holy Spirit will convict us of sin (John 16:8), but perhaps my heart was so hard or apathetic that he was unable to communicate to me. I just never felt guilty. But lately, I've been asking God to sensitize my heart so that when I do offend him or someone else, it bothers me. Now there's a gentle tugging in my conscience that won't go away until I properly confess my wrong.

Two dimensions of guilt

There are two dimensions to guilt—mental and emotional—and it's necessary to experience both. The mental aspect of guilt comes from cognitively acknowledging that something is wrong (*The speed limit is 55. I'm going 70; therefore, I'm breaking the law. The Bible says to be gentle. I just spoke harshly to my children; that must have been wrong*). The emotional aspect of guilt comes as we realize that our sin is not only wrong, but that it also hurts

God and others. This emotional response to our sin is called *godly sorrow* in the New Testament (2 Corinthians 7:10) and a *contrite heart* in the Old Testament (Psalm 51:17). According to 2 Corinthians 7:10, unless we enter into the emotionality of how our sin has hurt others (godly sorrow), we will probably not change. (In the Bible, repentance means to change.)

A testimony regarding the importance of the emotional dimension of guilt

For years, I gave mental assent to the fact that I had continually wronged my wife by having selfish priorities. I had placed my career above our marriage. I knew that was wrong, and I would often ask her forgiveness; but I would inevitably do it again. At that point there was no emotional dimension to my guilt or my confession; it was just cerebral. I cognitively knew it was wrong and that I needed to confess.

But one day I began to think about the emotional toll my sin had taken on my wife. I meditated on how deeply I had hurt her by my wrong priorities – how abandoned and embarrassed she must have felt attending our children's school functions alone, how worried she must have been when I failed to call to tell her I would be home late, and how unimportant she must have felt, being unable to get past my secretary on the phone. At that point my feelings of guilt took the 18-inch plunge from my head to my heart. I began to feel sorrow for what I had done.

Then I took it one step further. I realized that my sin had not only hurt my wife, but it had also hurt God. I personalized Isaiah 53: "He (Jesus) was bruised for my iniquities." Then I had this profoundly sobering thought - my sin, my wrong priorities, were part of why Christ had to die! My sin was partly responsible for why God had to hear his Son cry, "Father, why have you forsaken me?" That really shook me up.

When I realized my sin had deeply hurt both my wife and God, I became very sad inside. My sense of guilt reached a new dimension; I wasn't just giving mental assent to the fact that I had done wrong, I connected emotionally.

I confessed again to God and to my wife, but this time the emotional dimension was there. "Sweetheart, I realize now that my wrong priorities have hurt you deeply. I know it has caused you to feel neglected and at times unloved. I love you and don't ever want you to feel that way. Please forgive me."

I can't say that I've never messed up again, but I do know that after that encounter I had a new and intense resolve not to do it again. I guess that's what the Bible means when it says godly sorrow will lead to repentance.

When was the last time you entered into the *emotionality* of how you have wronged someone and you experienced godly sorrow?

Developing a sensitive conscience

God has given us a conscience through which he can speak to us when we have sinned. Our conscience is part of our spirit so it can act independently of our minds. That's why our conscience can be bothered even though our minds may not register the offense. God wants us to develop and maintain a sensitive conscience as opposed to one that is hardened and unresponsive (Hebrews 3:8). Our conscience remains pliable as we continually exercise the disciplines of confession and forgiveness.

Testimony about developing a sensitive conscience

One morning at work, I had a rather terse conversation with a fellow employee. At the time, I didn't think I had said anything wrong or offensive. But as soon as I left his office I had a nagging heaviness in my heart. Mentally, I couldn't figure out what was going on, but I knew that my spirit was troubled. I finally realized that my conscience was bothering me; I had offended my co-worker. I returned to his office and asked his forgiveness for my unkind words. I could tell by his reaction that I had indeed offended him and that he appreciated my apology. I'm glad I listened to my conscience.

The Antidote for Guilt - Confession

The biblical antidote for guilt is simple but profound. When we have wronged someone ("I've hurt you by my wrong priorities, critical spirit, selfishness, neglect, unkind words"), we need to confess and ask forgiveness.

Experiencing these two verses will bring freedom from guilt:
- 1 John 1:9 – *"If we confess our sins, he is faithful and just and will forgive us our sins and purify us from all unrighteousness."*
- James 5:16 – *"Therefore confess your sins to each other and pray for each other so that you may be healed."*

It's equally important to understand what will *not* remove guilt.

a. *Time will not eradicate guilt.* We often think that the more time that has passed since we sinned, the less influence our sin has and therefore our need to confess diminishes. "Yes, I hurt my wife. But that was twenty years ago, when we first got married." Regardless of how long ago it was that we sinned, we still need to confess.

b. *Our changed behavior will not eliminate our need to confess.* "Yes, I hurt my children with my temper, but now I've changed. I don't have a bad temper anymore." We rejoice in God's good work in your life, but you still need to confess.

c. *Suffering the consequences of sin will not remove guilt*. You may think that since you "paid the debt" your guilt is removed. "Yes, I sexually abused my daughter, but I spent five years in prison. I paid my debt to society." Even though society may pronounce you cleared, you still must confess to your daughter.

d. *Our offender forgiving us does not eliminate our need to confess*. "My husband is such a forgiving person. The other day I embarrassed him at a party and on the way home he forgave me – without my even asking." You are blessed to have a spouse who is quick to forgive, but his godliness is no excuse for your reluctance to confess.

There's only one thing that will remove guilt – confession.

How often should we confess? Obviously, as often as we sin, but another answer is "probably more than we have and do." For instance, if you're married, how long has it been since these words came out of your mouth: "Honey, what I did to you was wrong. Would you forgive me?" If you have children, how long has it been since each child heard these words: "Sweetheart, I was wrong. Would you forgive me?" 1 John 1:8 reminds us that "If we claim to be without sin, we deceive ourselves and the truth is not in us." Most of us would never claim to be "without sin"; yet our reluctance to confess is, in essence, the same thing. We are deceived and void of the truth.

There is a wonderful by-product of confession: healing. Look again at 1 John 1:9 and James 5:16. John tells us that our confession to God will *purify* us; James says that our confession to others will bring *healing*. Not only is our guilt removed through confession, but relationships are healed.

Now let's learn how to speak a genuine confession.

Characteristics of a good confession

1. The scope of our confession should be equal to the scope of our offense.

When we sin, to whom should we confess? For instance, if we just *think* poorly about someone but don't actually say or do anything, do we still need to confess to that person? The scope of our confession should be equal to the scope of our offense.

For instance, if we do not openly offend a person, we don't need to confess to her, but since God always knows our sins and he is offended by them, we always need to confess to him.

If I'm in the car with my spouse and two kids, and I speak unwholesome words to my spouse (a violation of Ephesians 4:29), it's not sufficient for me to confess to my spouse only. I should confess to God, my spouse, *and my children* since they were all in the scope of the offense. If our sin adversely affects a large group of people (an office staff, a church), we should confess to the group. All sin offends God so we must always confess to him (1 John 1:9). And when our sin offends others, we must confess to them as well (James 5:16).

2. Confessions are most effective if we take the initiative to confess without having to be confronted by those we offend.

Can you sense the difference in these two scenarios?

Scenario 1

> Joan - Hey, Bob. Got a minute?
> Bob - Sure, what's up?
> Joan - When we were having lunch yesterday, you said something that really offended me.
> Bob - Oh yeah? I'm sorry; what did I say?
> Joan - It was the comment about my work on the Meyer's project.
> Bob - Oh, that. Yeah, that probably did come across a little tacky. Would you forgive me?

Scenario 2

> Bob - Hi, Joan. Got a minute?
> Joan - Sure, what's up?
> Bob - Yesterday, when we had lunch together, I made a tacky comment about your work on the Meyer's project. It was wrong of me to say what I did. Would you forgive me?

This does not mean that we cannot and should not confront someone who has hurt us. It simply means that, from the standpoint of the one who has sinned, a confession will be more meaningful when initiated by the offender.

3. Our confession should have an emotional dimension to it.

Our sin is not only wrong; it also hurts those we offend. Therefore, a genuine confession should address the pain we have caused others. For instance, if we yell at our children it is not only technically wrong, but our children are hurt. We must confess not only to rid our own conscience of guilt, but also to show concern for their hurt. Therefore a good confession will often involve comforting words: "I'm so sorry that I hurt you by yelling at you." As mentioned earlier in this chapter, this emotion is called "godly sorrow" (2 Corinthians 7:10).

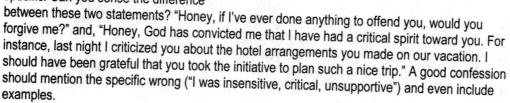

The Joy of Having a Clear Conscience
The story is told of a time when Sir Arthur Conan Doyle decided to play a practical joke on twelve of his friends. He sent them each a telegram that read, "Flee at once...all is discovered." Within twenty-four hours, all twelve had left the country.

4. Be specific. Name the sin.

Hurts don't come in generalities; they are specific, so our confession must be specific. Can you sense the difference between these two statements? "Honey, if I've ever done anything to offend you, would you forgive me?" and, "Honey, God has convicted me that I have had a critical spirit toward you. For instance, last night I criticized you about the hotel arrangements you made on our vacation. I should have been grateful that you took the initiative to plan such a nice trip." A good confession should mention the specific wrong ("I was insensitive, critical, unsupportive") and even include examples.

5. Use the phrase "I was wrong" instead of "I'm sorry."

The phrase "I'm sorry" implies little, if any, personal responsibility. It can even have several subtle meanings which can actually negate any sense of being wrong:
- "I'm sorry what I said offended you (but it wouldn't have offended you if you weren't so hyper-sensitive)."
- "I'm sorry you feel neglected (but after all, you are overly dependent)."
- "I'm sorry you were upset at the party (but no one else seemed to be)."

The phrase "I was wrong" acknowledges personal responsibility.

6. After saying, "I was wrong," refrain from saying anything else that might dilute the effectiveness of the confession.

Often, after we confess, we are tempted to do things like:

- **Minimize the offense** – "Yeah, I got mad, but that's not the main issue."
- **Rationalize/justify** – "The reason I got mad was..."
- **Blame others** – "I wouldn't have become angry if you hadn't..."
- **Offer a trite confession** – "Okay, I'm sorry."
- **Ignore the offense** – "Let's talk about something else."
- **Confess in order to avoid further conflict or embarrassment** – "Our company is coming soon; let's get this behind us."

Any attempt to rationalize, justify, or blame will dilute our confession. Even though what we're tempted to say may be true, it is inappropriate and counterproductive to discuss these issues at the same time we are confessing.

Of these six "substitutes" for confession, which do you most often struggle with?

_____

_____

Why are you often reluctant to speak a genuine confession?

_____

_____

7. Ask forgiveness.

The best way to do this is simply to ask, "Will you forgive me?" If you have genuinely and properly confessed and have exhibited godly sorrow over your actions, the ball has now been served into the offended party's court. It is now his decision whether or not to forgive you, but you should be free from guilt whether he does or doesn't. Even if he says, "No, I won't forgive you," you have done everything you can to right the wrong and should be released from feelings of guilt. In certain situations, particularly involving legal systems, restitution may still need to be paid (a fine for a speeding ticket, a jail sentence for a crime committed), but you should no longer have feelings of guilt.

8. To be thorough in our confession we should minister to the hurt we caused the other person(s).

In addition to admitting our wrong and asking forgiveness, it is appropriate and even beneficial to *comfort* those we have offended. This involves admitting that we not only *wronged* them but we *hurt* them. Words of comfort may sound like this: "*I know that when I criticized you, it really hurt you. I feel sad about that. It really grieves me that I hurt you.*"

When was the last time you confessed to someone and your confession had all eight of the *characteristics of a good confession* mentioned above?

Questions and answers regarding guilt

Question - I have a real problem with impatience. It seems that every other day I offend my wife or children. I've confessed to them a million times. Do I need to keep confessing every time I offend them with my impatience? Sometimes I get tired of confessing, and I'm beginning to think they even get weary of hearing it again.

Answer - Yes. Every time we wrong someone we need to confess. Even though the same offense is often repeated, every time we offend we must confess. Otherwise, the hurts and guilt will accumulate, and we may become apathetic about our sin. Whereas, if we continually confess, our constant confessing will hold us accountable for our sin and our need to change.

Question - Recently, I was in a situation where someone else wronged me. In the midst of discussing the matter, I said something to him I shouldn't have. My perspective on this is that his offense was a "$100.00 offense," and mine was a "$5.00 offense." He has not yet confessed to me his "big" offense, so I'm reluctant to confess my "small" offense. It just seems unfair for me to have to confess first.

Answer – We're not sure what "value" the two offenses had, but let's just assume your estimation is correct. Perhaps what you did wrong was small compared to what was done to you. Regardless, you need to confess what you did that was wrong. The fact that you were wronged does not justify your offense, and the fact that some issues are major and some minor has nothing to do with whether or not they should be confessed. Being faithful to confess even our small offenses will hold us accountable and teach us to be careful about how we react to those who have offended us.

Question - Years ago, when our children were at home, I had a real temper problem. My outbursts of anger were quite regular. I'm grateful to say that God did a deep work in my life in that area. I confessed my sin to God and my wife and have received forgiveness from both. And I have really changed. The last time my daughter visited us, she even commented on how different I am.

My question is - now that I've changed, do I still need to confess to my children that my outbursts of anger were wrong?

Answer - Yes, you need to confess to your children (and anyone else you might have offended by your temper). The fact that you have changed does not negate the fact that you sinned against your children. Even the fact that they see how God has worked in your life and that they're able to rejoice with you doesn't eliminate your need to confess to them.

And you must deal not only with the *wrongness* of your actions (by confession), but also with the *hurt* that you caused your children, by expressing godly sorrow to them and then comforting them.

It is important that you not allow your children to minimize what happened (*Dad, it's no big deal; that was a long time ago. Dad, don't worry about it; I can see how much you've changed.*) Help them get in touch with the hurt that they might have felt (*When I yelled at you in anger, you must have felt...belittled, betrayed, embarrassed, and confused. I'm so sorry I hurt you like that.*).

As God continues to work on areas of sin in our lives, his work is not complete until we both change *and* properly deal with the hurt our sin has caused others.

Question - The Lord has convicted me about a way in which I offended my spouse 25 years ago. I have confessed it to God and received his forgiveness. Do I need to confess it to my spouse?

Answer – It's good that you have heard from the Lord, and it is good that you have confessed your sin to him. But that's not enough. Your sin hurt two people: God and your spouse; and you need to confess to both. The fact that it happened 25 years ago does not negate your need to confess.

Question - I have recently felt guilt over some rebellious years I had as a teenager, but both of my parents are deceased. What can I do?

Answer - Sometimes we are convicted about a particular sin, but we're not able to respond to the offended person as we would like:

- We were rebellious toward a parent who is now deceased.
- We had an abortion.
- We violated someone and they refuse to talk to us.

If it is impossible to contact the person we offended, the following steps will help bring relief from guilt:

- Share with God your sorrow and confess to him.
- At an appropriate time and place, share your sorrow and grief with your journeymate and allow him to comfort you.

Question - I did something years ago that I'm very ashamed of. I've taken all the proper steps regarding confession, and I know that I have been forgiven; but it still haunts me. I can't seem to get over it.

Answer - One possibility is that you have not truly *received* forgiveness from God and others. We are often reluctant to receive forgiveness even when it is offered because we don't feel as if we deserve it; and the truth is, we don't! No one deserves forgiveness; it is a gift from God.

Another possibility is that Satan, the "accuser of the brothers" (Revelation 12:10), continues to accuse you even after you have properly confessed and received forgiveness. The best defense against his lies is to receive the truth that you have been forgiven and to bask in the gratefulness of it. Another good defense against his lies is to share your troubled thoughts with a friend and allow him to reaffirm the truth to you; you have been forgiven.

A third possibility is that feelings of guilt are being kept alive by the hurt that your sin caused you. This is a little difficult to explain, but we'll try.

One of the reasons God gave us rules (like the Ten Commandments) is to protect us from the hurt that sin produces. Sin not only offends, it also hurts.

- Our sin *offends* God because he is holy. Our sin also *hurts* God because it was our sin that caused Jesus to die.

- Our sin not only *offends* others but it also *hurts* them.
- But it's important to realize that our sin also hurts *us*. When we sin, we hurt God and others; but *we* also suffer.

In other words, God declared, "Don't lie," not only because our lying offends his holiness and our lying hurts others, but also because our lying hurts *us*.

You might need to meet with some Christian friends, share with them your struggles, and allow them to comfort you relative to the hurt that you sustained through your sin.

An officer in the army of Russian Czar Peter the Great was involved in a plot against the ruler. But though tortured terribly, the officer refused to confess.

Realizing that pain would not break him, Peter went up to the man, kissed him, and promised him that if he confessed he would receive not only a full pardon but a promotion to colonel. The officer was so unnerved by Peter's tactic that he embraced the czar and made a full confession. True to his word, Peter forgave the man and made him a colonel!

Although this example is certainly an imperfect one, the ending is worth noting. Full confession, full pardon -- and a promotion! That's just what God has provided for us if we will but confess our sins.

Discussion questions (Discuss these issues in your group or with your journeymate.)

1. What was the most interesting concept in this chapter?
2. Read Matthew 7:3-5. What can we learn from the "log and splinter" parable?
3. For a relationship to remain healthy, why is it important that confession and forgiveness be expressed on a regular basis?
4. If time allows, as a group, read and discuss the *Tale of Two Kings* handout that is located in the Facilitator's Guide.

Journeymate time (Discuss these issues with your journeymate.)

1. Share with your journeymate the results of your homework from last week.
2. Share with your journeymate your responses to the fill-in-the-blank sections in this week's lesson.
3. As you consider the emotional cup illustration, what guilt might be in your cup as a result of past offenses for which you've never confessed?
4. Are you quick to confess your faults or reluctant to do so?

Homework

1. Think of the people that you are relationally close to. If you're married, include your spouse, and if you have children, include them. As you consider each person, process through the following list.
    a. Alone, ask God to convict you of ways you have wronged this person.
    b. Meditate on the fact that what you did was not just technically wrong but that it also hurt this person. Allow God to sorrow your heart over your offense.
    c. Ask God to forgive you (1 John 4:9).
    d. At an appropriate time and place, share with this person your sorrow over hurting him. Confess to him, and ask his forgiveness (James 5:16).
2. As you reflect on your life, allow the Holy Spirit to convict you of offenses you might have committed years earlier that have never been properly resolved (For instance, *I unjustly fired an employee in anger. I stole money from my employer. I neglected my children when they were young.*) As you consider each incident, process through the steps given above.
3. Read Chapter 8 and complete the fill-in-the-blank sections.

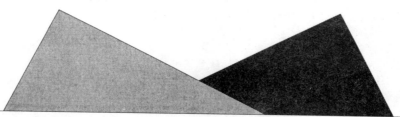

Chapter Summary

1. Feelings of guilt are actually a sign of spiritual and emotional health. When we wrong someone, we *should* feel guilty. But when guilt is unresolved and remains in our emotional cup, it will adversely affect us.

2. There is a mental dimension to guilt (*I acknowledge that what I did was wrong*) and an emotional dimension (*I deeply regret that I have wronged others because my sin has hurt them*). It is important to experience both.

3. Only a genuine confession can remove feelings of guilt. We should always confess to God because all sin offends him (1 John 1:9), and we should confess to those we have sinned against (James 5:16).

4. It is important to speak a genuine, thorough confession to those whom we have offended. Characteristics of a good confession include:
   a. The scope of our confession should be equal to the scope of our offense.
   b. Confessions are most effective if we take the initiative to confess without having to be confronted by those we offend.
   c. Enter into the emotionality of how you have hurt the other person.
   d. Be specific. Name the sin.
   e. Use the phrase "I was wrong" instead of "I'm sorry."
   f. After saying, "I was wrong," refrain from saying anything else that would dilute the effectiveness of the confession.
   g. Ask forgiveness.
   h. To be thorough in our confession we should minister to the hurt we caused. the other person(s).

Freedom from False Guilt

As discussed in Chapter 7, true guilt is a good emotion. When we have wronged someone, we *should* feel guilty. If we seldom have guilty feelings, it may be because our consciences are hardened, which is a dangerous condition. Again, God doesn't want guilt to *remain* in our hearts, and that's why he instructs us to confess our wrongs to both God and those we have offended.

But often we suffer from *false* guilt; we take moral responsibility for actions, events, and situations that were not our fault. False guilt has no value; it is always detrimental.

We did not include false guilt as one of the emotions in the emotional cup because false guilt is a specific expression of condemnation (which will be discussed further in the next chapter). But we have devoted an entire chapter to addressing some of the unique challenges of false guilt.

Where does false guilt come from? False accusations can come from other people *(It was **your** fault that our parents got a divorce.)*, from our own self-talk *(If I hadn't insisted on going out to dinner, we wouldn't have had the accident.)*, and from Satan, the "accuser of the brothers" (Revelation 12:10). Satan will never accuse us of sin that we indeed need to confess, for then we would be prompted to confess and find relief. The Holy Spirit will convict us of sin (John 16:8), but Satan will not. However, Satan (and others) may accuse us of

- ➤ Sins we have committed but properly confessed.
- ➤ Sins and hurts for which we are not responsible.
- ➤ Issues and actions that are not morally wrong and therefore do not need to be confessed.

Let's take a closer look at these three areas.

False guilt over sins we have committed but for which we have properly confessed.

When we sincerely confess our sins to God, he always forgives. When we confess our sins to other people, they may or may not forgive us. But regardless of how people respond, our sense of guilt should be removed. We may continue to sense regret over our actions, but we should not feel guilty.

But often, the accuser will continually remind us of past sins and suggest that the issue is unsettled. If we entertain his accusations, we'll become entangled in a no-win mind game of confessing sins that we have confessed before, only to find that relief is elusive. That's because false guilt cannot be neutralized by confession.

Do you ever struggle with feelings of guilt over sins which you have already confessed to God and received forgiveness? Explain.

False guilt over sins and hurts for which we are not responsible

Sometimes, we're involved in a hurtful and/or sinful situation, but we're not personally responsible for the sinful or hurtful acts. For instance

A child may feel false guilt over problems and conflicts his family is having.

- *Mom and dad are fighting again; it must be because of my grades at school.*
- *Our car got repossessed; it's probably because my doctor bills cost so much.*
- *My younger sister got busted for doing drugs. That wouldn't have happened if I were a better sister.*

A victim of abuse may feel personally responsible for the abuse.

- In an abusive relationship the victim may begin to feel guilty about her involvement. Particularly if the victim is a minor, she may not understand that although she was sinned against, she herself did not actually sin.

A testimony of how feelings of false guilt can develop from abuse.

My wife and I counseled a teenage girl who was really struggling. She was overweight, she didn't take care of her appearance, and her self-image was very low. In our first session she told us that for several years she had been sexually abused by an uncle. We were startled to hear that she thought it was her fault; she felt guilty about the abuse. She knew sexual immorality was wrong, and she knew she was involved in it; therefore, she concluded that she must be guilty. She also struggled with thoughts like, "Perhaps there was something about me that prompted my uncle to abuse me. Perhaps I was wrong in not resisting more fervently."

She also felt guilty that she had never told anyone. She knew, of course, that her uncle was also wrong but she erroneously bore the blame.

We simply told her the truth that although the sexual abuse was sin, it was not *her* sin. She had been sinned *against*, but her involvement was innocent.

First, we mourned with her about the hurt and pain that she sustained during the years of abuse. We particularly grieved with her that she had borne her pain *alone* for so long. She wept and we comforted her. I'll never forget the look on her face when she received the truth. For years she had carried the burden of false guilt, but now she was free.

We may feel responsible for hurtful incidents over which we had no control.

- *If I hadn't suggested we go out to eat, we wouldn't have had the wreck.*
- *I couldn't attend my daughter's piano recital because my plane had mechanical problems and was five hours late. She was so disappointed.*
- *I was in charge of the school picnic, and we had to cancel it because of rain.*

Do you ever accept responsibility for hurtful and/or even sinful situations that you have no legitimate responsibility for? Explain.

_____

_____

_____

False guilt over issues that are not wrong

We may confuse issues that are unfortunate or even hurtful with issues which are actually wrong. We should not feel guilt over the former, although feelings of sorrow and sadness may be appropriate.

- *I had ten kids audition for the main characters in the play. There were only three parts, so I know seven of the kids were sorely disappointed. I feel so bad about it.*
- *Our company is downsizing, so I had to release several good employees. I feel awful about it.*
- *I had to discipline my four-year old because she disobeyed me. She cried a lot. Did I do something wrong?*

Do you struggle with false guilt over issues that are not actually wrong, although they may involve sorrow and disappointment? Explain.

_____

_____

_____

Protection against false guilt

Here are some practical ways to avoid false guilt:

1. "Filter" your thoughts.

Learn to filter questionable thoughts through several layers of scriptural truth. Unhealthy thoughts will have a hard time surviving. For instance, send troubling, guilt-ridden thoughts through the "filter" of Philippians 4:8: "Finally brothers, whatever is true, whatever is noble, whatever is right, whatever is pure, whatever is lovely, whatever is admirable—think about such things."

If your thoughts make it all the way through the filter, you may continue to dwell on them. But if they get "caught," discard them.

Think of some thoughts and feelings you've been struggling with lately. Send them through the Philippians 4:8 "filter." Record here what happens. For example, "I realize now that I shouldn't feel guilty about having to release some of my employees. It's not my responsibility."

_____

_____

_____

_____

2. Share your thoughts with a journeymate.

In Chapter 1 we encouraged you to spend time every day emotionally debriefing with another person. During that time, it would also be advantageous to talk about the significant *thoughts* that you had during the day, particularly those thoughts which were troubling or confusing or ones that might have caused you to feel bad about yourself. It's amazing how clearly someone else can see through the fog of accusations and deception and minister truth to us.

Freedom from false guilt

What is the biblical antidote for false guilt? Knowing and receiving truth.

Knowing truth

In John 8:32, Jesus declared that *"Then you will know the truth, and the truth will set you free."* In other words, as we replace lies with the truth, false guilt will be dislodged.
- *I'm not responsible for my mom and dad's arguments.*
- *The sexual abuse I experienced was not my fault.*
- *There's nothing wrong with disciplining my children.*

Receiving truth

But there's also an emotional dimension to false guilt which must be dealt with on an emotional level.

Have you ever noticed that it's possible to intellectually know certain Bible verses and yet struggle with experiencing what they promise? There seems to be a "legal/mental" aspect of truth and an "experiential/emotional" side. For instance, it's possible to mentally know that
- "I am fearfully and wonderfully made" (Psalm 139:4)—and yet feel inadequate, unlovely and inept.
- I have been forgiven (1 John 1:9)—but still struggle with forgiving myself.
- I need not be fearful (1 John 4:18)—but still be gripped by fear.
- God has compassion on me (2 Corinthians 1:3-4)—yet remain in my hurt and pain.
- God has a wonderful future for me (Jeremiah 29:11)—but be anxious about the future.

So how can truth take the 18-inch plunge from our head to our heart? How can truth impact us emotionally? Sometimes we need help from others.

Allowing others to confirm truth to us

Sometimes lies can become planted so deeply in our hearts that we need more than one person to minister truth to us. We need the confirming testimony of two or three witnesses.

"A matter must be established by the testimony of two or three witnesses" (Deuteronomy 19:15).

"But if he will not listen, take one or two others along, so that every matter may be established by the testimony of two or three witnesses. I tell you the truth, whatever you bind on earth will be bound in heaven, and whatever you loose on earth will be loosed in heaven. Again, I tell you that if two of you on earth agree about anything you ask for, it will be done for you by my Father in heaven. For where two or three come together in my name, there am I with them" (Matthew 18:16,18-20).

Here's a testimony about how the body of Christ ministered healing to a young woman who had suffered from guilt regarding an issue which she had repeatedly confessed to God.

Kay was 16 years old when she had an abortion. At the time, it deceptively seemed like the only option, and she had a lot of support from those who proclaimed her right to "choose." But deep in her heart, she was troubled and distressed to think that she might have done the wrong thing.

During her second year of college, Kay attended a campus Bible study where, for the first time, she heard the gospel message. She was particularly interested in the "forgiveness of sins" aspect of the message because for years she had carried an enormous burden of guilt regarding her abortion. One night, the teacher presented the plan of salvation and invited those attending to receive God's gift of eternal life. That night Kay entered into a personal relationship with Christ.

During her senior year, she fell in love with Bob, a fine Christian boy; and after graduating, they were engaged to be married. During premarital counseling, they shared with each other their past journeys, and Kay told Bob about her abortion. He lovingly responded, "Sweetheart, that's okay, I love you anyway." It was never brought up again.

During the ensuing years, they began raising a family and became active in a church. They both developed a genuine heart for God and his Word and, year after year, became more aware of God's love for them. But there was a persistent nagging in Kay's soul that she couldn't escape. She still felt guilty about her abortion.

Mentally, she knew all the right answers. She had memorized 1 John 1:9, Micah 7:18 and other passages dealing with forgiveness and had even pictured herself as the woman caught in adultery, to whom the Lord said, "Neither do I condemn you" (John 8:11). She meditated on Romans 8:1, "Therefore, there is now no condemnation for those who are in Christ Jesus," but the feelings of guilt remained.

Let's take a break in this story to discuss a simple but powerful biblical principle: the confirming of truth by "two or more witnesses." Then we'll return to Kay's testimony.

In Matthew 18, Jesus taught his disciples some kingdom principles about dealing with relationships. Placed between a discussion on "how to deal with a brother who is sinning" and the issue of "how many times should I forgive my brother," Jesus explained several truths.

1. Issues can be confirmed by the testimony of two or three witnesses (Matthew 18:16).

There is power in the joint declaration of Christians. It's often important for more than one person to confirm an issue. This corroboration can confirm a specific event (in Matthew 18 a brother had sinned), and can be powerfully used to affirm the truth of God's Word. When two or three Christians "agree" on a biblical truth, they are not *validating* the Word of God, for it is true whether or not we agree with it. They are simply confirming together (and perhaps confirming *to* another Christian) what God has already declared as truth.

2. We have the ability and authority to bind and loose on earth, that which is bound and loosed in heaven (Matthew 18:18).

When we gather together and "confirm" a matter, we are simply declaring to be true what God has established in the heavens (Psalm 119:89). For instance, we can confirm to people that their sins have been forgiven because God's Word declares it to be true; we can affirm a person's worth because God has already established it.

3. When we engage in this joint accomplishment, he will be with us (Matthew 18:20).

When we faithfully minister the Word of Christ, we are assured that Christ will stand by us and will ratify what we say and do.

This is the powerful principle behind the "one-anothers" of Scripture. For instance, we are told to comfort one another (2 Corinthians 1:4), love one another (John 15:12), forgive one another (Colossians 3:13), and accept one another (Romans 15:7). God is the source of all of these divine commodities, but we often need two or three witnesses to confirm to us what God has already provided for us and declared about us.

This confirmation process through relationships is one way that *mental* truth can become *experienced* truth. In Kay's situation, she mentally knows that God has forgiven her, but she's had difficulty in *receiving* the truth and appropriating the freedom that comes from experiencing biblical truth.

Let's return to our story and see how Kay is ministered to by her "two or three witnesses"—her friends.

One Friday night, Kay and Bob have their best friends, Janet and Mike, over for dinner. After they finish eating, they play several board games and then talk through some "Questions for Interaction." They progress through a series of questions, starting with "Where did you live between the ages of 6 and 12?" to "What is the most exciting thing going on in your life at the present?" to "What's the best thing that has ever happened to you?" The fourth question is, "What's the most disappointing thing that has ever happened to you?" When it's Kay's turn to share, she begins to weep quietly.

Bob - (Gently putting his arm around her) Sweetheart, what's the matter?
Kay – I'm still struggling to get over it.
Bob - Kay, I know what you're thinking; I'm so sorry.
Kay - We've talked about it so many times before.

Mike - Kay, if you want Janet and me to leave the room, we will.

Kay - Oh, no, that's fine. Bob and I have talked about this before, and I've even shared this as part of my testimony. In fact, Bob and I have even talked about sharing this with you when the time is right. (Bob nods to reassure Kay the time is right.)

When I was 16 years old I had an abortion. I felt guilty about it then, and even since becoming a Christian, I just can't get over it. I've often cried out to God and asked Him to forgive me, and I know he has; but it still haunts me. (Janet moves her chair closer to Kay, close enough to hold her hand.)

Janet—I'm so sorry. (Janet embraces Kay and cries with her.)

(For about ten minutes, Janet, Mike, and Bob minister comfort to Kay's hurt, allowing her to grieve her pain. Then they confirm to her, God's forgiveness.)

Mike - Kay, I really messed up when I was a teenager. One night after a football game, I was drinking and driving with some friends when I lost control of my car. We had a bad wreck, and one of my friends was seriously injured. He lived, but he's walked with a limp ever since. I asked for his and God's forgiveness, but Janet will tell you, I had a hard time forgiving myself.

Kay - How did you finally deal with it?

Janet - It was in a similar situation as tonight. We were in a small group Bible study with some Christian friends. We really felt safe with them, and we had already discussed the fact that one day God might want Mike to share with others what had happened. Mike finally had the nerve to tell his story. He had never really shared it with anyone but me. The group ministered to his pain and then shared the truth of God's forgiveness to him, and that night he was set free.

Bob - Sweetheart, God really has forgiven you.

Kay - I understand that mentally, but for some reason my heart still feels dirty.

Mike - Kay, he forgave me for what I did, and he has forgiven you. Gratefully receive it. I know I was blessed by Paul's statement in Romans 8, "Therefore, there is now no condemnation for those who are in Christ Jesus." Paul had persecuted the Jews and watched Stephen be murdered, yet he was able to give thanks to God because he was forgiven through Christ and now he was free.

Janet - We don't deserve his cleansing, but that's part of God's grace poured out on us. Have you ever thought of the truth that on the day you became a child of his, God already knew everything wrong you had done - including the abortion - and everything you would do wrong in the future? Yet, with no explanation other than love, he decided on that day to make you his child anyway!

Kay - I never thought of it that way. He chose to love me no matter what.

Mike – That's right. And God doesn't want you to suffer from guilt anymore. He wants you to walk in freedom.

Kay – I've wanted to believe that.

Bob - Can all three of us pray for you? I believe God is setting you free - right now.

Kay - (With a sense of relief) Oh, please...that would mean so much to me.

❖ Where two or three are gathered in my name, I will be there.
❖ Whatever you loose on earth will be loosed in heaven.
❖ A matter must be established by two or three witnesses.

Kay knew the truth—God had forgiven her—and her husband had reinforced the truth to her, but it took three "witnesses" to really confirm the matter in her heart.

Discussion Questions (Discuss these issues in your group or with your journeymate.)

1. What was the most interesting concept presented in this chapter?
2. 1 Kings 21:1-16 tells the story about Naboth, who was falsely accused by two men and then stoned to death. Is it possible that in the course of our lives, we have been falsely accused by more than one false witness? Why is it hard to break free from this type of bondage?
3. Why does it sometimes take more than one person to minister truth and freedom to us?
4. Is anyone in your group troubled by an issue which might be clarified and ministered to by "two or three witnesses?"

Journeymate time (Discuss these issues with your journeymate.)

1. Share with your journeymate the results of your homework from last week.
2. Share with your journeymate your responses to the fill-in-the-blank sections in this week's lesson.
3. What false guilt might you be suffering from? Share this with your journeymate and minister to one another.

Homework (To be completed before the next meeting.)

1. Meet with your journeymate during the week to continue pursuing freedom from false guilt.
2. Read Chapter 9 and complete the fill-in-the blank sections.

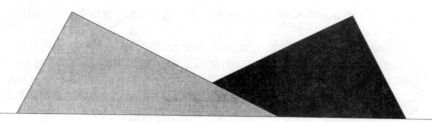

Chapter Summary

1. Whereas true guilt is a healthy emotion (if properly processed), false guilt is always detrimental and debilitating. False guilt comes from being falsely accused by Satan, others, and self.

2. We are susceptible to false guilt when we are accused of
   a. Sins we may have committed but have properly confessed.
   b. Sins and hurts for which we are not responsible.
   c. Issues and actions that are not morally wrong and therefore do not need to be confessed.

3. We can protect ourselves from false guilt by continually filtering our thoughts to analyze where they are coming from and recognizing whether or not they are true, and by sharing our thoughts with a journeymate so she can provide objectivity and perspective to what we are thinking.

4. Freedom from false guilt comes as we know and receive truth. Often, we may need others to confirm truth to us (Matthew 18:16, 18-20).

Freedom from Condemnation

In the realm of human experience, there are positive emotions – *"I feel happy, affirmed, contented, hopeful"* and there are painful emotions – *"I feel embarrassed, used, neglected, frustrated."* Though no one wants to experience painful emotions, they are a natural part of life. No one wants to be embarrassed, used, frustrated, or neglected, but most people realize that, to some extent, painful emotions are inevitable.

But there is one heart-wrenching, spiritually-debilitating emotion that God never wants us to experience, one that we should never accept as just a "part of life": condemnation.

Condemnation means to judge as unfit, to pronounce sentence, punishment, or judgment. In the life of a believer, this sense of worthlessness is not from God. There is no condemnation because Christ took the sentence, punishment, and judgment for our sin (Romans 8:1-3).

Condemnation might cause us to think

- *I can't do anything right.*
- *I'll never be as good as other people.*
- *I'm a terrible person.*
- *I'm not important to anyone.*
- *It's all my fault.*
- *I'm not worthy of receiving your love.*

In contrast, God would say to us

- Your soul is more valuable than everything that is in the world (Luke 9:25).
- I loved and valued you so much that I gave my Son for you (John 3:16).
- I have accepted you, just as you are (Romans 5:8, 15:7).
- You are of great value to me (Matthew 6:25-34).

Many people suffer under the burden of condemnation; it clings to their soul like barnacles on the side of a ship. It is part of the Satan's strategy to "kill, steal, and destroy" the abundant life that God has promised us (John 10:10).

Where does condemnation come from? Often, from other people. For instance, consider every person you spend time with and ask yourself this question about the relationship: *Does this relationship cause me to feel better about myself or worse about myself?* If a particular relationship makes you feel poorly about yourself, it may be that condemnation is being dispensed.

We can also suffer from *self*-condemnation. Are you quick to take out the proverbial hammer and hit yourself over the head? Are you quick to say, "I'm sorry," even when you're not responsible for what happened? If so, you may be beating yourself up with self-condemnation.

And of course, Satan will also try to condemn us.

We should never accept condemnation. Titus 2:15 teaches us: "Do not let anyone despise you." When someone tries to make us feel bad about ourselves, we should reject their suggestions. God also desires that we be set free from feelings of condemnation we have encountered in the past, that we not minister condemnation to others, and that we become lovingly involved in helping others be set free.

We'll begin our discussion of condemnation by clarifying the difference between conviction and condemnation.

Condemnation contrasted with conviction

It's important to know the difference between condemnation and conviction. True conviction is good for us (healthy thoughts and emotions that lead us to repentance), but thoughts and feelings of condemnation are unhealthy.

Relative to the *source* of condemnation and conviction:
Condemnation comes from Satan, others, and our self.
Conviction comes from the Holy Spirit.

Satan, the accuser of the brethren (Revelation 12:10), ministers condemnation: "You've sinned again—the same sin you confessed yesterday. You're having a problem in this area because there's something really wrong with you. God is getting tired of hearing your confessions. Just admit it. You're a failure."

Other people can minister condemnation to us by speaking hurtful lies: "You'll never amount to anything," "Why can't you do anything right?" or subtle phrases such as, "Just let me do it." "Your brother does this much better than you do." "That was okay, but do better next time."

"Self-talk" can also get us into trouble. For instance, perhaps you've been looking forward to having lunch with a friend you haven't seen in several months. He calls the morning of your lunch appointment and leaves a message on your voice mail: "Something's come up; I won't be able to meet you for lunch today." A rather innocent phone message, but self-condemnation can take this harmless message and quickly spin it out of control: "He probably just didn't want to take the time to eat lunch with me... He probably doesn't like me...I'm not sure if anyone likes me...I'm not sure I'm likeable...I don't even think I'm worth anyone liking me."

Conviction comes from the Holy Spirit, "When he (the Holy Spirit) comes, he will convict the world of guilt in regard to sin and righteousness and judgment" (John 16:8). But condemnation does not come from God, "For God did not send his Son into the world to condemn the world, but to save the world through him" (John 3:17).

The Pharisees once brought to Jesus a woman who had been caught in the act of adultery. They were condemning her and had, no doubt, hoped that Jesus would sanction their assault. Jesus addressed her sin but did not condemn her, "Neither do I condemn you, go now and leave your life of sin" (John 8:3-11).

Relative to the *nature* of condemnation and conviction:
Condemnation is general in nature.
Conviction is always specific.

Condemnation communicates a general, somewhat elusive attack: "You're a liar, a worthless person, a terrible Christian"; whereas, guilt is always specific: "What you said at lunch today was a lie." Condemnation leaves us frustrated (how do we deal with "You're a liar; you're a worthless person"), but guilt is specific enough that we can properly deal with it through confession: "Father, forgive me for telling a lie at lunch today."

Relative to the *point of attack* by condemnation and conviction:
> *Condemnation attacks who we are—our identity.*
> *Conviction addresses specific acts that we have done.*

Condemnation attempts to tear down our worth as human beings: "You're worthless. You'll never amount to anything. You'll never change"; whereas, conviction addresses specific acts, things we did or didn't do: "You were insensitive to your spouse. You neglected your son."

Through the provision God has made for us in Christ, he separates "who we are" from "what we do." God says to the believer, "I love you and accept you regardless of what you do or don't do. I can love you and hate your sin at the same time. What I think about your sin will not affect my love toward you." That's the basis upon which Paul declares, "While we were yet sinners, Christ died for us" (Romans 5:8).

Relative to how condemnation and conviction affect our sense of hope:
> *Condemnation ultimately steals hope for the future.*
> *Conviction can ultimately produce hope.*

Condemnation produces hopelessness, despair, discouragement, despondency, and gloom. If I am a worthless person, there's no hope.

Conviction, though it initially produces somber feelings of godly sorrow, can ultimately produce feelings of hope, expectation, and confidence. Knowing that God loves me, regardless of my sin, gives me confidence that the essence of our relationship will not be affected by what I do. The fact that God has provided a way for me to deal properly with my sins (through my confession and his forgiveness) gives me hope.

Relative to our proper response to condemnation and conviction:
> *When feeling condemned, we should reject the lie and embrace the truth.*
> *When feeling convicted, we should confess.*

Condemnation is always based on lies. We must identify the lies, reject them, and gratefully receive the truth, particularly focusing on God's truth concerning our identity in Christ.

Sometimes this process can be even more fully experienced as we share our thoughts and struggles with a journeymate because we can benefit from the loving, empathetic care of a loved one to help dispel the lie and to affirm to us the truth. "Every matter may be established by the testimony of two or three witnesses" (Matthew 18:16).

The proper response to guilt and conviction is to experience godly sorrow (2 Corinthians 7:10), confess to all offended parties (1 John 1:9, James 5:16), and receive God's forgiveness.

Can you discern the difference between conviction and condemnation in your life? When was the last time the Holy Spirit convicted you of sin? Write about it here:

When was the last time you entertained condemning thoughts? Write about it here:

Origins of Condemnation

How does condemnation get into our emotional cup? Through what channels is it distributed?

1. Criticism

There is a difference between constructive correction and harmful criticism. It is often acceptable and necessary to correct and admonish someone's behavior, but it is never okay to criticize a person for who he is. We must separate *who people are* (precious souls created in the image of God) from *what they do* (unproductive, inappropriate, or sinful behavior). We can and should address wrong behavior: "Sally, you forgot to clean up your room," but never demean a person's character: "Sally, you never do anything right; you're worthless."

Even proper correction of wrong behavior should be balanced by generous doses of praise and appreciation. If all we ever do is correct someone's behavior, even though the correction may be legitimate and warranted, feelings of self-condemnation may develop. A good rule-of-thumb might be that for every time we tell someone what he did wrong, we should make four or more comments on what he did that was right.

Also, insensitive phrases said "in jest" or in an attempt to be humorous should be avoided, for after the laughter subsides, the hurtful words remain. ("John, you are clueless." "Susan, have you been asleep for the past six months?") Even nicknames spoken "in fun" (Bozo, Fat Man) can lead to condemnation.

2. Comparisons

Unhealthy comparisons are fertile ground for feelings of self-condemnation.

- *Why aren't you as good as...*
- *I'm going to give the project to Bob; he always does a great job.*
- *Susan, your brother never had trouble in math.*
- *If you only had as much faith as...*

Whether or not the comparison is accurate is not the issue (perhaps Susan's brother *is* better at math). The point is, we should never try to establish or deny a person's worth by comparing him or her to another person. The fact that every person is uniquely fashioned by God makes comparisons unfair and biased. (Perhaps Susan's brother is better at math, but Susan is better at music.) Instead of comparing one person's weakness with another person's strength, we should simply compliment each person's strengths.

Even seemingly "healthy" comparisons should be used with caution. To tell a 7th grader "You play basketball just like Michael Jordan," will probably produce positive thoughts and feelings (even though the child is aware of the exaggeration). But to say to the same child, "You play basketball just as well as your older brother used to play," may produce unhealthy thoughts and feelings (*It's important that I live up to my brother's reputation. My parents judge my performance based on the standard set by my brother. In what other areas do my parents compare me to my brother? What will happen if I don't play as well as my brother?*).

3. Neglect

Under-involvement in a person's life can lead to feelings of self-condemnation (*If I was different, or a better person, then I would receive the attention and affection I long for.*) Lack of attention may cause someone to assume, "I guess I'm not important because no one wants to spend time with me." A lack of affection may produce feelings of, "I'm not lovable." If a person's need for respect is neglected, he or she may think, "My opinion is of no value; perhaps I have no value." If we neglect to comfort someone when he is hurting, he may think, "It must be my fault that I'm hurting; I deserve the pain."

Also, if special occasions such as birthdays and anniversaries are continually overlooked, that neglect may cause us to think that our lives are unimportant to others. On the contrary, when we lovingly meet someone's needs, we affirm his value as a unique and significant person.

4. Emphasis on performance

An emphasis on "doing" versus "being" will generate feelings of condemnation. If my significance as a human being is directly tied to what I do instead of who I am, my sense of value or worth may be inextricably influenced by a "high-jump" mentality. This produces inordinate expectations, "As soon as you successfully conquer one height, I'm going to raise the bar again," exhausting expectations, "You're okay as long as you keep jumping," and anxious feelings, "What will happen to me when I can no longer jump that high?"

5. Verbal, physical, or sexual abuse

Victims of abuse often believe that they are responsible for the abuse and that they deserve it. They may think: "Perhaps the negative statements said about me are true." "I probably deserve the physical abuse I'm receiving; I must be a bad person." "Because of who I am, I attracted the sexual abuse; I'm the culprit."

Because of the natural admiration and trust that children have for their parents, abuse sustained in childhood can easily be misunderstood and quickly lead to feelings of condemnation. A child may think, "No one knows me better than my mom and dad. If they say I'm a bad person, it must be true. If they abuse me, I must deserve it."

6. Elevating personal opinions and convictions to the level of biblical absolutes

Whenever we knowingly or unknowingly demand or expect someone to abide by our personal convictions or preferences, we may be in danger of ministering condemnation.

There is a difference between a biblical absolute ("Thou shalt not steal") and a personal conviction ("I sense God's leadership for me to read my Bible every morning before I go to work"). We must differentiate between standards that God has set for *every* believer in his Word from ways he has personally led each of us. It's important to encourage others to embrace biblical absolutes, but we should not expect people to adhere to our personal convictions or preferences.

7. Fearful control

Fear will often cause a person to be overly controlling. His thought process may progress like this:
a. "Because of unresolved pain in the past, I'm afraid of what may happen in the future."
b. "If I can control my future, the probability of my getting hurt will diminish."
c. "Therefore, I'm going to control my environment, the people around me, and the agenda."
d. "I don't like it when you challenge my control."

e. "I don't like your differences because they confuse me and I can't control them. You need to be like me."

f. "There's something wrong with you because you're not like me!"

8. Perfectionism

Being around a perfectionist can lead to feelings of condemnation. For instance, consider the impact of growing up with parents who were perfectionists:

- *I can't ever clean my room as well as mom wants it cleaned. Is there something wrong with me?*
- *Dad is always correcting my grammar. What's wrong with me?*

We may eventually feel that we can never do enough, and what we do is never good enough.

9. Reluctance to assume responsibility for offenses

Relationships inevitably bring disappointment and hurt. Harsh words are uttered, tempers flare, and priorities become misplaced. For relationships to remain healthy, each individual must assume responsibility for his or her inappropriate behavior, words, and attitude. When someone refuses to assume his responsibility (for example, a parent or spouse), someone else may begin to assume the guilt, and condemnation can easily follow. For instance, if a child spills his milk and his father blows up in anger at him, but the father doesn't take responsibility for his anger by confessing that it is wrong, the child may think, "Dad wouldn't have lost his temper if I had not spilt my milk. It's all my fault that he got upset and yelled." To the contrary, if the father confesses his temper and asks forgiveness, the child will understand that he was not responsible for the offense.

Read the following examples of ways in which we may inadvertently minister condemnation to others (consider in particular how you relate to your spouse, children, co-workers, and friends). On a scale of 1 - 10 (1 being "I don't really struggle with this" and 10 being "I struggle with this a lot"), consider to what extent you may be ministering condemnation to others.

_____ *I sometimes have a critical spirit. If there's 90% right and 10% wrong, I usually comment on what's wrong.*

_____ *I sometimes compare people. At times I'll even try to motivate people by comparing them to the most "successful" person around.*

_____ *I may not be as conscientious about meeting people's needs as I should be, particularly those closest to me.*

_____ *I often put a real premium on performance. I'm a "get it done" type person, and this may cause me to judge a person based on how much he or she can produce.*

_____ *I can be rather ruthless with my tongue. If I'm not careful, I can degrade a person and really make him feel bad about himself.*

_____ *I'm an opinionated individual. I always have a pronounced preference in any situation, and I don't mind sharing it. I realize, though, that I often expect others to concur with my opinion, and I may make them feel bad if they don't.*

_____ *I often try to control my environment (and everyone in it).*

_____ *I'm often reluctant to accept responsibility for my mistakes. If I don't accept responsibility, other people who are innocent may think that they have done something wrong.*

_____ *I have strong personal convictions which I believe are from the Lord, but I realize now that I have often tried to make others abide by my personal convictions.*

As you reflect on these nine origins of condemnation, which ones might you have suffered from as a child? How has this affected your sense of self-worth?

_____

_____

_____

Protection against condemnation

We should be careful not to minister condemnation to others. The list of origins (given above) are things we must *avoid* doing (don't criticize or compare people, etc.), but there are also some things we can pro-actively *do* to help protect others from condemnation.

Generous and frequent doses of acceptance and approval will help guard against condemnation. When we accept someone we are saying, "I receive you (accept you) just the way you are. Regardless of how you look, your past failures, idiosyncrasies—I accept and love you just the way you are. God fashioned you in a very unique way, and I receive and embrace that." When we minister approval to someone we are saying, "You are of great value, significance and worth. I applaud the good things you do and the godly character that you exhibit but regardless of the 'good things' you do, I value you as a person."

As we accept and approve of people, their sense of self-worth will be fortified, helping to protect them against condemnation.

We must also encourage others (particularly our children) not to try to "live up" to what God has chosen to do in our own lives. This is particularly important in the lives of children who have a "successful" parent. If you are a successful minister, lawyer, writer, public speaker, athlete, make a concerted effort to "release" your children from thinking they have to live up to what you are. Lead them to discover the unique path that God has ordained for them.

Symptoms of condemnation

When we suffer from condemnation, we may display one or more of the following symptoms:

1. Self-directed anger – "I'm so upset at myself."

As condemnation prompts me to question my sense of value or worth, I'll be frequently disappointed in and angry at myself. This low-grade but persistent anger often keeps me from being gentle and compassionate toward others; I may eventually become hard and calloused.

2. Self-initiated fear – "I'll probably fail at..." "I can't trust that..."

Feelings of condemnation may cause me to become pessimistic about the future. As I focus on perceived inadequacies and failures, I become fearful of the future. This fear may cause me to be reclusive and hesitant to be open and vulnerable with others. I'm afraid if people get to know me, they'll reject me. This fear also hinders trust and can prompt judging of others: "You don't care about me; you don't mean what you're saying."

3. Self-blame – "If something bad happens, it must be my fault."

Feelings of condemnation may cause me to be quick to blame myself when things go wrong. Instead of making a rational assessment of what went wrong, I'll prematurely assume that I was the problem. I'll keep an imaginary hammer close by which I take out several times a day and hit myself on the head. Self-blame is often being expressed when someone says "I'm sorry" a lot, even though he was not an integral part of the situation. This self-blame makes a person vulnerable to abuse by others who refuse to take responsibility for their own actions.

4. Self-abuse – "I'm a terrible person; therefore I'm going to punish myself."

Condemnation often leads to self-abuse, which can take many forms: inordinate and unnecessary abstinence ("I'm not going to allow myself to do things I enjoy doing"), physical abuse (eating disorders, self-mutilation), neglect ("I'm not going to take care of myself regarding proper grooming and appearance"), and even suicide.

5. Reluctance to receive – "I'm not worthy of receiving that."

An individual who suffers from condemnation will often be reluctant to receive. When compliments are offered, the typical response is, "Oh, it's no big deal." When attention is given, the attitude is, "Wouldn't you rather spend time with someone else?" When comfort is offered, the response is, "Oh, I'm okay" or "Other people took a worse hit than I did." This reluctance to receive hinders gratitude and the joy God intends for us to experience.

6. Reluctance and inability to give – "Why should I give to you?"

Condemnation may inhibit our ability and desire to give to others. Our attitude may be, "I really don't have anything to contribute; besides, no one needs me because I'm not valuable." Also, an inability to receive (see #5 above) will always short-circuit our ability to give, simply because we cannot sustain giving without receiving. If we do give, it will be out of duty and obligation, not gratitude. Life becomes an endurance race, and we miss out on abundant living.

7. Reluctance to share needs and hurts – "I won't bother telling you what my needs are."

"I'm hesitant to share my needs because I'm not worth having my needs met anyway. I'm reluctant to share my hurt because it was probably my fault. Even if you sought to minister to my needs or comfort my hurt, I would not believe it was genuine."

8. Reluctance to admit wrong – "I'm not going to admit that what I did was wrong because that would mean I'm a bad person."

If I think that my value as a human being is based on what I do, and not on who I am, when I do wrong things, I will be reluctant to admit that I did something wrong because that would be admitting that I am a "wrong" person. From this misunderstanding, a defensive attitude may develop.

9. Reluctance to forgive myself – "I can't forgive myself because I'm a bad, worthless person."

Condemnation so undermines my sense of dignity and value that it's hard to embrace the truth that God has forgiven me and declared me worthy in Christ. I don't deserve to be forgiven.

10. Tendency to condemn others – "I'm not okay and neither are you."

We tend to deal with other people using the same set of rules we have adopted for ourselves. If my value is based on performance, so is yours. If I didn't have my needs met growing up, why should you? Since I'm always being compared to others, how do you measure up?

Also, since condemnation often rises and falls on "who's good and who's bad," making you look bad makes me look good. The more I point out your inadequacies, the better I feel about myself.

11. Reluctance to serve – "Why should I minister to you?"

In John 13:3-5 we are told why Jesus was able to serve his disciples, even on the night of his betrayal: "Jesus knew that the Father had put all things under his power, and that he had come from God and was returning to God; so he got up from the meal, took off his outer clothing, and wrapped a towel around his waist...and began to wash his disciples' feet."

Jesus did not suffer from any condemnation. He knew exactly who he was, where he had come from, and where he was going. And from that state of security, confidence, and contentment, he served.

To the contrary, if we are unsure of our own personal worth and value and are insecure about who we are (these feelings often accompany condemnation), we will be reluctant to serve.

12. Reluctance to forgive – "I'm a miserable person so I want you to be also. My forgiving you would help us both, but I'm not going to do it."

A person who suffers from condemnation may be reluctant to forgive for several different reasons:

- *I have a hard time understanding the fact that although I do wrong things (I sin), I am still a person of value. Because I feel that way about myself, I'm going to feel that way about you. When you offend me, I'll be reluctant to forgive because I still think that you are a bad person.*
- *Forgiveness brings healing to a relationship. I'm not sure I want our relationship to be healthy.*
- *Because I am reluctant to receive forgiveness (see # 9 above), I'll be reluctant to give it to others.*

Review the twelve symptoms we've just discussed. Which do you struggle with the most and how are they manifested in your life? (For instance, *I have a lot of self-directed anger. I'm really hard on myself when I make a mistake. It's hard for me to admit when I'm wrong.*)

_____

_____

Freedom from Condemnation

Appropriating Freedom

During World War II, Lieutenant General Jonathan Mayhew Wainright was commander of the Allied Forces in the Philippines. On May 6, 1942, following a heroic resistance of enemy forces, he was forced to surrender Corregidor and the survivors of the Philippine campaign. For three years he suffered as a prisoner of war in a Manchurian camp.

During his interment, he endured the incessant cruelties of malnutrition, physical and verbal abuse, and psychological mind games. Through it all, he maintained his dignity as a human being and soldier.

But after the war ended, his captors continued to keep Wainwright and the other prisoners incarcerated. The war was over, but the bondage continued. One day an Allied plane landed in a field near the prison. Through the fence that surrounded the compound, an airman informed General Wainwright of the enemy's surrender and the American victory.

Wainright immediately pulled his emaciated body to attention, turned and marched toward the command house, burst through the door, marched up to the camp's commanding officer and said, "My commander-in-chief has conquered your commander-in-chief. I am now in charge of this camp." In response to Wainwright's declaration, the officer removed his sword, laid it on the table, and surrendered his command.

For those who know Christ as Lord and Savior, the good news is this: Our Commander-in-Chief has conquered our enemies.

Even though it is legally and positionally so, many Christians continue to live under the debilitating bondage of condemnation because they don't understand or appropriate the victory and freedom that have already been provided. They stay in their inner prison, waiting for victory and subsequent deliverance. As long as the enemy keeps us bound, he can bluff us into accepting a defeatist attitude in which we think our only hope of freedom is "in the sweet by-and-by, when we shall meet on that beautiful shore."

But God's promise of freedom is present tense:

- "But thanks be to God! He gives us the victory through our Lord Jesus Christ" (1 Corinthians 15:57).
- "Therefore, there is now no condemnation for those who are in Christ Jesus" (Romans 8:1).

How to be free from condemnation

Principle 1 – Don't deal with condemnation alone.

The Apostle Peter describes Satan as a roaring lion who is looking for *someone* to devour (1 Peter 5:8). The analogy is accurate because a lion won't attack a pack of animals; it waits until its prey is isolated from the rest of the group and then strikes when its victim is alone.

When condemning thoughts and feelings come, share them with a journeymate; don't try to resist them alone. "Though one may be overpowered, two can defend themselves. A cord of three strands is not quickly broken" (Ecclesiastes 4:12). Sometimes one other person isn't enough; it often takes the witness of two or three fellow believers to confirm truth to our hearts. This underscores the importance of having a group of close friends and loved ones with whom we can be open and vulnerable. It speaks powerfully to those who are married and to families: a deep, intimate marriage and close family ties help keep us safe. When we vulnerably share with those who care for us on a regular basis, we keep ourselves in a safe environment. We stay close to "the pack." When the enemy attacks, we're not far from help.

Principle 2 - Identify areas in which you suffer from condemnation.

It is helpful and even necessary to identify specific areas of bondage. There are several ways to do this:

1. Study the possibilities.

Condemnation can have such a subtle hold on us, we don't even know we're in bondage. Here's a list of some patterns and thoughts of condemnation. Do any of them apply to you?

- I basically don't like myself.
- I feel inferior to others.
- I have a hard time forgiving myself.
- I can't get freedom from some sins.
- I can't seem to do anything right.
- I'm not important to anyone.
- It's all my fault.
- I'm not worthy of your loving me or meeting my needs.
- I'll never be as good as other people.
- I'll never change.
- I'll never get over my wrong choices.
- I'm not as good as...
- I've got to do more and do it better.
- I deserve any pain that I receive.

2. Identify any symptoms of condemnation you may suffer from (see the symptoms listed on pages 111-113).

3. Ask your journeymate to help you identify ways in which you suffer from condemnation.

Particularly when we are deceived or are in denial, it often takes another person to identify ways in which we suffer from condemnation.

4. Pray and ask for the Holy Spirit's discernment.

Jesus taught us that "When he, the Spirit of truth, comes, he will guide you into all truth" (John 16:13). If we ask him to, the Lord will show us areas in which we suffer from condemnation. Sincerely ask him and trust that he will show you. You might want to pray the same prayer the psalmist prayed: "Search me, O God, and know my heart; test me and know my anxious thoughts. See if there is any offensive way in me" (Psalm 139:23-24).

5. Analyze recurring symptomatic problems.

Recurring symptoms (like those which flow from a full emotional cup) are often indicative of unresolved emotions. Analyze these symptoms and try to discern if they are rooted in condemnation.

Principle 3 - If possible, identify the sources of the condemnation.

The "truth that sets us free" not only includes identifying feelings of condemnation but also understanding the sources of the condemnation.

- I realize now that I often felt physically inept when I was frequently compared to my older sister who always excelled in sports.

- I realize now that I have felt like a failure as a pastor's wife. Our former church thought, and communicated to me, that all pastors' wives should be outgoing leaders. That's just not me. I began to feel inadequate because I didn't fit their preconceived mold.
- I realize that I have felt mentally and academically inferior. I never finished high school, and our society puts such a premium on education.
- I realize now that I have felt unimportant. In my family of origin I had six younger siblings, and there didn't seem to be enough attention to go around. I felt more like another parent to my siblings than a cherished child.

Principle 4 - Identify the lie behind the condemnation and embrace the truth.

Condemnation begins with and is sustained by lies. These lies must be exposed and countered with truth.

- The lie, "You'll never amount to anything," can be countered with the truth based on Jeremiah 29:11 - God has a wonderful, unique, and meaningful plan for your life.
- The lie, "You're weird," can be countered with the truth that you were fearfully and wonderfully made by God; he sees you as the apple of his eye (Psalm 139:14).
- The lie, "I'm not important to anyone," can be countered with the fact that 1 Corinthians 12 says that you are a unique part of the body of Christ; the body needs you to be complete.
- The lie, "I'm not worthy to receive your love," can be countered with the truth from Ephesians 3:17-19 which says that agape love cannot be earned or deserved. It is unconditional, unmerited and free.

Principle 5 - Gratefully receive the fact that God separates who you are (declared worthy through Christ's death) from what you do (whether it's positive performance or painful sin).

God is able to distinguish between who we are (we were created in the image of God and are objects of his love) and our fallen nature (we are sinners by nature and choice). Even though he cannot tolerate our sin, he loves us. It's obvious that his love motivated him to meet our needs, in spite of our sins, for "God demonstrated his own love for us in this: While we were still sinners, Christ died for us" (Romans 5:8).

Condemnation focuses on our wrongs and then uses our sin to taint our concept of who we are ("I sin; therefore, I'm a terrible person, and God's love of me has been forfeited."). It also attempts to place a permanence on our sin ("You sinned; God will never forgive you,"), particularly sins that we continue to commit ("You've done it again. God's tired of hearing you confess that sin. Just live with it.").

The truth is, we are fearfully and wonderfully made, fully accepted, deeply loved, highly treasured and precious in God's sight. That's who we are!

Accepting the awe and wonder of the Father's grace and gratefully receiving the Father's love frees our soul and guards our heart from the accuser's attack. Will any of our sins ever take God by surprise? Did he not make provision for us in Christ on the day we became his children? Did he not know all about our past and future and choose to receive us as his own anyway?

Rejecting condemnation

God never wants us to suffer from thoughts and feelings of condemnation. The apostle Paul instructed his friend Titus, and us, "Do not let anyone despise you" (Titus 2:15). When anyone tries to shame us or condemn us, we should reject his suggestions.

If someone says, "You'll never amount to anything," it is appropriate to reply, "That is not true. I will become all that God has intended for me to be, and his intentions toward me are good." If someone says, "You're not as good in math as your brother," we may rightly respond, "My worth as a person has nothing to do with my brother's math skills."

If someone tries to shame you by suggesting, "You're a bad person," you can, with all confidence say, "You're wrong. I may do wrong things, and we all do, but I'm not a bad person." Our rejecting condemnation should not be misunderstood as rebellion against authority. For instance, if a wife refuses to accept condemning statements from her husband, she is not being rebellious; she's simply obeying Titus 2:15. Likewise, a child should not receive condemnation from his parents; that is not what "Children, obey your parents in the Lord" means.

Free to love others

In Matthew 22:36, a Pharisee asked Jesus what he thought would be a difficult question for Jesus to answer, "Teacher, which is the greatest commandment in the Law?" Jesus said, "Love the Lord your God." Jesus also clarified what was the second greatest commandment, "Love your neighbor as yourself." In the Great Commandment we are told that our love should flow in three directions: God, others and ourselves. The second commandment infers that our love for others will be hindered *unless* we love ourselves.

Obviously, Jesus was not advocating a selfish, egotistical, self-absorbed type of love, since that would violate the other directives of love (God and others) and would contradict other verses which encourage a selfless type of love (John 15:13, 1 Corinthians 13:5). He was simply affirming our value as individuals (we are worth being loved), giving us permission to feel good about ourselves (it's okay to love ourselves) and establishing the fact that if we don't think well of ourselves (love ourselves), we'll have difficulty loving others.

- If I can't accept myself, blemishes and all, why should I accept you with your blemishes?
- If I don't believe I am of great value, why should I value you?
- If I don't understand that God looks beyond my sinful deeds and loves me as a person, why should I look beyond your sin and love you?

What hinders us from loving ourselves? Condemnation.

The more we suffer from condemnation the less we like ourselves. And to some degree, when we don't like ourselves, we're not free to totally love others as we should. Condemnation may also hinder our love for God because we may

- Resent him for the way he made us. (I'm inferior. I don't like myself. God made me the way I am; therefore, I resent him.)
- Think we're unworthy of his love. (I'm such a terrible person, God couldn't love me; therefore, I won't bother to love him.)

As we are released from condemnation, we will be able to more fully and thoroughly love God and others. God's desire and provision for us is summarized in Romans 8:1, "There is now no condemnation for those who are in Christ Jesus."

Discussion questions (Discuss these issues in your group or with your journeymate.)

1. What was the most interesting concept presented in this chapter?
2. Read these five verses: John 13:23, 19:26, 20:2, 21:7, 21:20. The phrase, "The disciple whom Jesus loved" refers to the apostle John. Who wrote these five verses? What does this tell us about the author's self-image?
3. If time allows, read and process the handout "Christians - Ministers of Condemnation?" that is located in the Facilitator's Guide.

Journeymate Time (Discuss these issues with your journeymate.)

1. Share with your journeymate areas of condemnation that you may struggle with and consider where the condemnation might have come from. Identify both the lie that the condemnation is based upon and the truth about the issue. (Example: *During grade school I was sick a lot and had to miss a lot of school; so I always felt behind. One year I even had to repeat a grade in school, and my classmates who were promoted to the next grade level made fun of me. Since that time I have always thought of myself as a slow learner, and I really struggle with feelings of inferiority and worthlessness.* The journeymate responds with this truth: *Missing school a lot probably did affect you academically, but that doesn't mean you're a slow learner; besides that, your academic achievements have nothing to do with your worth as an individual. You are precious in God's eyes and in mine. I know that what happened to you during your school years must have hurt a lot. I'm sorry that it happened. I hurt for you because I love you and care for you.*)
2. In order to be free from condemnation, it's important to receive and embrace what God says about us. Read the handout entitled *Our True Identity in Christ* (in the Facilitator's Guide). There is a list of verses which reveal what *God* says about you. You and your journeymate may take turns speaking the verses to each other.
3. Condemnation often grips us so tightly that it takes more than one person to confirm the truth to us. (Refer again to the section called "Allowing Others to Confirm Truth to Us" at the end of chapter 8). If this is the case, arrange to meet with some other people and share with them your struggles with condemnation.

Homework (To be completed before the next meeting.)

1. Plan to meet with your journeymate this week and continue to work on any condemnation that may be in your cup.
2. Read again the ways in which you might have ministered condemnation to others (pages 108-111) and be particularly careful to avoid doing it this week.
3. Read Chapter 10 and complete the fill-in-the-blank sections.

Chapter Summary

1. Condemnation is an attack on who I am as a person, my sense of self-worth. Condemnation causes me to feel bad about myself. I begin to think there's something wrong with me.

2. There is a difference between condemnation and conviction. Conviction is from the Holy Spirit and leads to freedom; condemnation is not of God and leads to bondage.

3. There are many *origins* of condemnation; feelings of condemnation may come from various sources. By learning to identify these sources, we will be able to discern how we and others may have been victimized, and we will learn how to avoid further exposure to condemnation in our lives and in the lives of others.

4. There are many *symptoms* of condemnation. Feelings of condemnation will cause us to behave in certain ways. By learning to recognize these symptoms in ourselves and others, we will be able to minister freedom.

5. This chapter identifies five principles of freedom from condemnation.

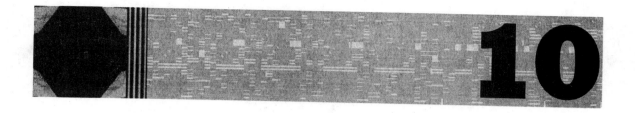

Freedom from Stress

"Sometimes I get the feeling that the whole world is against me,
but deep down I know that's not true.
Some of the smaller countries are neutral." *Robert Orben*

There's no doubt that we live in a stress-filled society. And the factors that cause stress will likely increase. Interestingly, a limited amount of stress is good and necessary for healthy living. If we live a stress free life we will likely become apathetic and unproductive. But severe amounts of stress and continuous stress will wreak havoc with our emotions. The question is: How can we achieve a balance and keep stress from filling up our emotional cups?

Romans 15: 4 says, "For everything that was written in the past was written to teach us, so that through endurance and *the encouragement of the Scriptures we might have hope.*" So let's consider some Scriptures which may offer a remedy for stress.

First we'll look at Psalm 131.

"My heart is not proud, O Lord, my eyes are not haughty. I do not concern myself with great matters or things too wonderful for me. But I have stilled and quieted my soul; like a weaned child with its mother, like a weaned child is my soul within me. O Israel, put your hope in the Lord both now and forevermore" (Psalm 131).

Let's discuss one phrase at a time.

"I do not concern myself with great matters or things too wonderful for me" (verse 1).

It's amazing to think that David—King of Israel—slayer of giants—would encounter "great matters" and that he would consider certain things "too wonderful for him." And yet he acknowledged that there were, indeed, areas so far outside his comfort zone that he would avoid them. He was a great musician, but perhaps public speaking made him nervous. He was a valiant warrior, but perhaps he got frustrated with financial management. He might have been a visionary, but perhaps he got stressed out over details. Regardless of the specifics, David did acknowledge that there were areas in which he felt uncomfortable and that he was going to avoid those areas.

Our stress level begins to escalate when we are continually asked to perform tasks which are far outside our comfort zone and when we're expected to "be" someone we're not.

What's the solution?

1. Discover who you are and what you feel comfortable doing.
2. Accept the way God has made you.
3. Learn to say "no" to matters that are "too wonderful."

In Psalm 131, it's interesting to note that David's confession of his inadequacies is prefaced by a declaration of humility, "My heart is not proud, O Lord, my eyes are not haughty." Pride will prompt us to cling stubbornly to "great matters" while humility will encourage us to release them.

Three testimonies about how having to do something "too wonderful" can cause stress.

❖ I am the chief programmer for a computer software firm. I helped develop the main program that we sell, so I was a natural candidate for training our customers to use it. I started out training two or three people at a time, which was fine; but a year ago my boss asked me to begin teaching large training classes. Sometimes there are 40-50 people in the room. Quite frankly, I can't stand it! I get so nervous up in front of people. I thought I would get used to it, but it has only gotten worse. I'm always stressed out over it.

❖ I'm a pastor's wife. Two years ago my husband and I moved to a new church. The former pastor's wife was vivacious, extroverted, and enjoyed maintaining a high profile in the church and community. I'm just not like that. I've always been quiet-natured, and I'm happy to stay in the background and serve others. But there's a constant pressure on me at church to be like the former pastor's wife. I finally gave into that pressure and have tried for months to meet everyone's expectations, but I feel so uncomfortable.

❖ I'm married to a man who, figuratively speaking, can keep eleven plates spinning at one time. He's really quite amazing. He can manage five major projects at work, three at the church, two at home, and he's starting a business on the side. He not only manages to keep up with all this, he actually thrives on it! For several years I tried to be involved in everything he was involved in, but I eventually got frustrated and burned out. I had to learn my limits, choose what was best, and say "no" to the rest.

What tasks are you asked to perform regularly which are so far outside of your comfort zone that they have become "great matters" to you?

_____

_____

What can you do to eliminate this stress?

_____

_____

Do you feel pressured to "be" someone that is really not "you"? Explain.

_____

_____

"But I have stilled and quieted my soul; like a weaned child with its mother, like a weaned child is my soul within me" (verse 2).

The Psalmist learned to value and experience times of quietness and repose with the Lord. He uses the metaphor of a child in the loving care of its mother. David probably first learned the value of time alone with God when he was a shepherd boy tending sheep on the Judean hillside. But it no doubt became a regular time of solace for him throughout his life. For example, as an adult, when he was being chased by Saul and his own men were threatening to mutiny, the Bible records that David "Found strength in the Lord his God" (1 Samuel 30:6).

An effective way to relieve stress is to spend quiet moments with God on a regular basis and more so during periods of high stress.

The quality of time we're describing is not synonymous just with "time off." This is not the same as, "What are you going to do on your day off? Watch T.V.? Sleep late? Play golf?" These are quiet moments *with God.*

Out of 24 hours in a day, why not spend a few quiet moments "like a weaned child with your father" - your heavenly Father.

Stress Stats
- Stress has been linked to all the leading causes of death, including heart disease, cancer, lung ailments, accidents, cirrhosis, and suicide.
- 75-90% of visits to primary care physicians are due to stress-related problems.
- An estimated one million workers are absent each workday because of stress-related complaints.
- 40% of all worker turnover is due to job stress.

Spend the next five minutes with the heavenly Father. It's not necessary to say a lot during this time. This is not the time to process through a prayer list. Anticipate that God might talk to you. When you're through, record your thoughts here.

_____

_____

"O Israel, put your hope in the Lord both now and forevermore" (verse 3).

During difficult times it's important to have hope, even if it's just a glimmer. If we are subject to stress and difficulties and have no hope, we soon slip into despair. Even Jesus was able to endure the shame of the cross because of the "joy set before him" (Hebrews 12:2). By faith he could see the hope of the resurrection, his bride, and his impending glory. And Jesus' hope was in his Father (Luke 23:46).

In like manner, we need hope to make it through stressful times. But in what will we place our hope? The Psalmist said, "Some trust in chariots and some in horses, but we trust in the name of the Lord our God" (Psalm 20:7). A modern interpretation would say, "Some trust in bank accounts and some in human ability, but we trust in the name of the Lord our God." Hope is future-oriented. It doesn't help us deal with the past, but it gives us confidence for the future. During stressful times, it's reassuring to know that our future is in his hands.

If you feel led, write out a prayer to God in which you state that your hope and trust is in him.

Here are some other Scriptures which will help us deal with stress:

"Cast all your anxiety on him because he cares for you" (1 Peter 5:7).

The Lord has graciously given us permission to throw our cares on him. The motivation behind this courteous and kindhearted offer is that he cares for us. We can cast our cares (noun) on him because he cares (verb) for us. It's so simple; don't miss it.

Testimony about casting our cares on the Lord.

I pastor a large church, so in the course of the average week, I encounter myriad problems - building new buildings, financial pressure, meetings, sermon preparation, and counseling. My wife and I recently left to go on a two-week vacation. As we were driving out of the city, I realized that my mind was plagued with cares and worries. If I didn't do something about it, my vacation would be ruined. When we got to the city limits, I pulled my car over to the side of the highway, got out of my car, walked over into the grass, cupped my hands together and verbally listed all the cares I could think of. I then cast them upon the Lord (I ceremoniously dumped them onto the ground), reckoned that they now belonged to him, and vowed not to think about them for the next two weeks. We had a wonderful vacation.

Make a list of your cares and anxieties (*I'm worried about paying my bills. I'm anxious about my job. I'm concerned about my child.*)

_____

_____

_____

Now, cast them upon the Lord.

"He has showed you, O man, what is good. And what does the Lord require of you? To act justly and to love mercy and to walk humbly with your God" (Micah 6:8).

"Make it your ambition to lead a quiet life, to mind your own business and to work with your hands, just as we told you" (1 Thessalonians 4:11).

These two verses speak to the value of pursuing a simple but God-honoring lifestyle.

Sometimes in life we feel compelled to maintain a certain profile of "success," a standard of "excellence," and a high level of achievement. A quick glimpse into eternity puts things into perspective. A million years from now only three things will exist which exist today: God, his Word, and people.

Our striving, and the accompanying stress it brings, will subside if we will adopt a simple but focused outlook on life. Easy to say, hard to do.

In what ways have you been trying to maintain an unnecessary and perhaps unrealistic lifestyle?

_____

_____

_____

Discussion Questions (Discuss these issues in your group or with your journeymate.)

1. What was the most interesting concept presented in this chapter?
2. At the beginning of this chapter, it was mentioned that a certain amount of stress in life is necessary and good. Read this statement by Mihaly Csikszentmihalyi, author of *Flow*, and discuss the balance we need to achieve in our lives, relative to stress: "The best moments in our lives usually occur when a person's body or mind is stretched to its limits in a voluntary effort to accomplish something difficult and worthwhile."
3. What is the primary source of stress in your life right now?
4. If time allows, take one of the *Stress Tests* found in the Facilitator's Guide.

Journeymate time (Discuss these issues with your journeymate.)

1. Share with your journeymate the results of your homework from last week.
2. Share with your journeymate your responses to the fill-in-the-blank sections in this week's lesson.
3. Talk about acute areas of stress that you may be experiencing and then pray for one another.

Homework

1. Plan to meet with your journeymate this week and continue to work on any stress issues that may be in your cup.
2. Read Chapter 11 and complete the fill-in-the-blank sections.

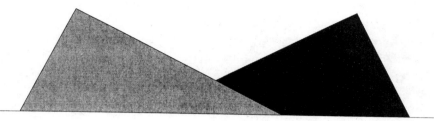

Chapter Summary

1. Stress is not all bad. A limited, controlled amount of stress is necessary in our lives to keep us sharp and active. But most people are overly stressed, often to the point of emotional duress.

2. Sometime we are under severe stress because we're trying to do things that God did not "program" us to do, and we're trying to "be" someone we're not.

3. We should schedule times of rest to balance out the stress in our lives.

4. We should learn to exercise trust in the sovereign Lord and regularly "cast our cares" upon him.

5. To reduce stress in our lives, we might need to simplify our lives.

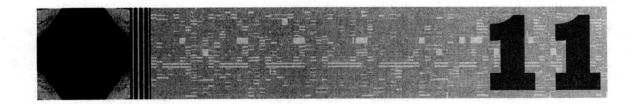

Filling Our Emotional Cup with Positive Emotions

[Note: This chapter is based on another workbook by Ferguson, McMinn, and Walter – *Top 10 Relational Needs*, which would be a good follow-up study to this workbook.]

Throughout this workbook we've used the emotional cup illustration to explain how painful emotions can accumulate within us and, in time, adversely affect our lives. Fortunately, God's word gives clear instruction on how to "empty" our cups of these emotions.

But God's desire is not that we simply have a cup that is *void of painful emotions;* he wants us to have a cup that is *full of positive emotions*. In this chapter we'll discuss the concept of developing a healthy emotional state.

Replacing painful emotions with positive emotions

Picture a glass filled with dirty water. There are two ways to replace the dirty water with clean water. One approach is to begin to pour clean water into the glass and let it spill over until eventually, all the dirty water is replaced with the clean. Another approach is to simply tip the glass over, pour out the dirty water, and then add the clean.

Relative to transforming our inner emotional cup, a combination of both approaches is ideal, although often, some emptying has to take place before significant filling can occur. The emotional cups of some people are so full of painful emotions that they are not able to receive anything positive. In other words, if you struggle with a huge amount of hurt, anger, fear, guilt, and condemnation, you might have a hard time receiving approval, support, and encouragement. As discussed in Chapter Three, we really do have a limited emotional capacity, so often we have to empty some emotions before we can receive others.

Painful emotions remain; positive emotions must be replenished

This sounds entirely unfair but unfortunately it's true. Painful emotions seem to have a longer life-expectancy than positive emotions. For instance, if you experience a deep hurt and it remains unresolved, it can plague you for years. Receive a nice compliment from your spouse, and it may stay with you for a while but then, in time, you need to hear it again. We need a steady, constant input of positive emotions.

For instance, one of our main emotional needs is appreciation, and this need must be continually replenished. It's not a matter of, "I received a lot of appreciation when I was a child; therefore, I don't need any more of it." We will need to hear words of appreciation for the rest of our lives.

Positive emotions will produce positive spillage.

Look again at the emotional cup illustration on page 26. Notice the sad and destructive symptoms of an emotional cup that is filled with painful emotions. The "spillage" isn't very pretty. Now picture an emotional cup filled to overflowing with positive emotions. In this case, what might the "spillage" look like?

Ten positive emotions that we all need

Here is a brief description of ten positive emotions that we need to be "filled up with." For each emotion, we have discussed how God has met this particular need in our lives and how we can minister each need to others.

1. I feel *accepted*

Acceptance involves receiving and loving another person willingly and unconditionally, especially when he is "different" from us and even when his behavior is irritating or even offensive.

"Accept one another, then, just as Christ accepted you, in order to bring praise to God" (Romans 15:7).

Jesus met our ultimate need for acceptance in that "while we were yet sinners" he died for us (Romans 5:8). He looked beyond our faults and saw and met our needs. During his earthly ministry, Jesus accepted people regardless of background, race, or condition (the Samaritan woman, the thief on the cross, the Gentile Centurion, the woman caught in adultery). He helped people deal with their failures (Peter's denial, disciples' lack of faith); loved all people unconditionally, and forgave freely ("Father forgive them").

We are convinced of God's continual acceptance of us because he taught the apostle Paul that "God has shown me that I should not call any man impure or unclean" (Acts 10:28).

How can we minister acceptance to other people?
1. Look beyond people's faults and minister to their needs. The closer we get to others, the more we notice their imperfections. Acceptance requires that we look past these flaws and meet their needs.
2. Quickly forgive others when personally offended. Unforgiveness short-circuits acceptance.
3. Help people to deal properly with their failures and disappointments. Our need for acceptance is accentuated when we experience a failure or when we are unduly disappointed. We need to notice when people experience a failure (real or perceived), or when they're disappointed (particularly in themselves) and minister to their need for acceptance. Acceptance is based upon a person's innate value to God as a person of special worth and not on performance or productivity.
4. Love people with God's unmerited, unconditional, and unlimited love. God's love for us is unmerited (we don't deserve it and can't earn it), unconditional (it's not

based on what we do or don't do), and unlimited (it will never "run out" or be detained). We should accept and love others in like manner.

5. Be particularly sensitive to accept people who are in any way different from you. If people look, talk, or dress differently, have different customs, are of a different nationality or socio-economic background, or for any other reason are in the minority, they may have a significant need for acceptance.

6. Be especially sensitive to other people's need for acceptance when they enter into a new environment. When people move to a different city, school, church, or job, they have an acute need to be accepted into the new group.

2. I feel blessed by your *affection*.

The need for affection is met by expressing care and closeness through physical touch and tender words.

"Greet one another with a holy kiss" (Romans 16:16).
"And he took the children in his arms, put his hands on them and blessed them" (Mark 10:16).

During his earthly ministry, Jesus frequently ministered to others through physical touch. When Jesus healed, he often did so accompanied by physical touch (Matthew 8:3, 8:15, 9:29); he consoled his disciples accompanied by physical touch (Matthew 17:7); and he ministered to children through physical affection (Mark 10:16, Matthew 19:13).

How can we minister affection to other people?

1. Give affection through physical touch. The appropriateness of certain gestures will be determined by the relationship:
   - **Spouse** – hold, caress, give body rub, hold hands, and kiss. Many married couples can benefit from increased non-sexual expressions of affection.
   - **Your own children** – hold, kiss, hold hands, wrestle, and hug.
   - **Other children** – hug, hold hands in an affirming manner, and kiss on the forehead.
   - **Friends** – shake hands, hug, slap on the back, embrace.
2. Verbalize your love; speak tender phrases of endearment. It's particularly meaningful to speak unsolicited, spontaneous expressions. For instance, say, "I've been thinking today about how special you are to me and how much I love you." If you have difficulty speaking words of love and affection, begin by writing your thoughts on cards and notes, then progress to verbal communication.

3. I feel *appreciated*.

The need for appreciation is met through expressing thanks, praise, and commendation, particularly recognizing someone's accomplishments or efforts.

"And be thankful" (Colossians 3:15b).
"I praise you" (1 Corinthians 11:2).

God meets our need for appreciation as the Bible affirms us as saints (Romans 1:7), sons (Ephesians 1:5), joint heirs (Romans 8:17), royal priests, and a people for God's own possession (1 Peter 2:9).

During his earthly ministry, Jesus continually voiced appreciation to individuals: the Canaanite woman (Matthew 15:28), Mary of Bethany (Mark 14:6), a Centurion (Luke 7:9), John the Baptist (Luke 7:28), and a poor widow (Luke 21:3). God has also promised to affirm and appreciate those who are faithful (2 Timothy 4:8, Luke 6:35, Ephesians 6:8).

How can we minister appreciation to other people?
1. Praise people verbally and publicly. When someone demonstrates a positive attitude or character trait or performs a positive deed, praise her. Verbal praise is particularly effective when stated *publicly*. It's good to praise a spouse, friend, child, or employee privately, but to praise her *in front of other people* is usually even better.
2. Focus on what people do that is right, not just on what they do that is wrong. Don't have a "sin patrol" mentally—always trying to catch people doing something wrong. Instead, try to catch people doing something right and then verbally and publicly praise them. Your spouse, children, employees, and friends will be more motivated by positive affirmation than by negative comments.
3. Generously give cards, trophies, plaques, and special gifts. Physical tokens of appreciation are very effective and usually long-lasting. The monetary value of a gift is relatively unimportant; it's the thought and effort that counts. Special, individualized gifts are particularly effective. Become familiar with people's hobbies, what they collect, their favorite foods and drinks, and give them gifts that are unique to their interests.

4. I feel *approved* of.

The need for approval is met by building up or affirming a person and acknowledging the importance of a relationship. Approval also involves noticing and affirming positive character qualities—affirming people for *who* they are, not just for what they *do*.

A powerful example of approval occurred at Jesus' baptism. God the Father met his Son's need for approval when he said, "You are my beloved Son with whom I am well pleased" (Mark 1:11NAS). He affirmed that their relationship **existed** ("You are *my* Son") and that it was **important** ("my *beloved* Son").

During his earthly ministry, Jesus frequently expressed approval to various people. He affirmed a generous widow (Mark 12:41-44), Peter (Matthew 16:13-19), the devoted Mary of Bethany who sat at Jesus' feet (Luke 10:38-42) and who anointed him with perfume for burial (John 12:2-9), a Centurion with great faith (Matthew 8:5-10), and a grateful leper (Luke 17:11-19).

God has met our ultimate need for approval, affirming us as saints (Romans 1:7), sons of the Most High (Ephesians 1:5), joint-heirs with Christ (Romans 8:17), royal priests and people for God's own possession (1 Peter 2:9), and as his dearly loved children (Ephesians 5:1, 1 John 3:1).

How can we minister approval to other people?

1. Affirm people privately and publicly as being of great value to you and to God: "You are my friend; I'm so fortunate to have a friend like you!" "I'm so blessed to have you as my Dad." "I couldn't ask for a better boss/secretary/co-worker than you!"
2. Affirm people for who they are and for character qualities they exhibit such as diligence, gentleness, honesty, purity, dependability, faithfulness, punctuality, compassion, joyfulness and initiative. "Bill, you are one of the most responsible people

I know. Your diligence and thoroughness are excellent qualities."

3. Especially seek to meet this need within your immediate family. If you are married, tell your spouse, "God has blessed me so much through you as my wife/husband. You are a blessing to me!" If you have children, tell them, "I'm so proud you're my daughter." "You're my beloved son in whom I am well pleased!" "God could not have given me a more special son/daughter."

5. I feel blessed by your *attention*.

The need for attention is met by conveying appropriate interest, concern, and care for another person. We meet people's need for attention when we take thought of them, particularly when we enter into their "world."

"But that the members (of the body) should have the same care for one another" (1 Corinthians 12:25NAS).

Jesus met our ultimate need for attention by leaving his world (heaven) and entering into our world. He became like us so that we could know him and have a personal relationship with him. During his earthly ministry Jesus didn't spend time just with the masses but invested a lot of time with individuals (Zacchaeus, Nicodemus, the Samaritan woman, the disciples).

God continues to meet our need for attention by providing us with the medium of prayer whereby we may receive his individual, undivided, and unlimited attention. Furthermore, we are convinced of the individual attention he gives us because the Bible says that he knows our thoughts (Psalm 139:2), counts the number of hairs on our head (Luke 12:7), knew us in our mother's womb (Psalm 139:13), and promises to provide for our every need (Matthew 6:25-34).

How can we minister attention to other people?

1. Spend **time** with people. There's no substitute for spending time with people. Time is a valuable commodity; therefore it's a wonderful expression of attention.
2. Spend **individual** time with people. Don't just spend time with groups of people; arrange for private time with individuals because a person's need for attention cannot be met in groups. For instance, if you have three children, in order to meet each child's need for attention, you should spend private time with each child.
3. Meet people where they are—enter into **their** world. Have lunch with your child at *her* school. If you have a business luncheon, pick up your client at *his* office. When your spouse, friend, or child has a recital, concert, game, program, or awards ceremony— be there.
4. **Listen** to people. Don't dominate conversations but encourage others to talk and to talk about themselves: their feelings, goals and plans. Try to talk where there won't be any interruptions and concentrate on the conversation. Don't daydream or succumb to distractions.

6. I feel *comforted*.

The need for comfort is met by properly responding to a hurting person with appropriate words, feelings, and physical touch. Comfort involves entering into another person's grief and pain.

> "Weep with those who weep" (Romans 12:15b).
> "The God of all comfort, who comforts us in all our troubles, so that we can comfort those in any trouble" (2 Corinthians 1:3, 4).

Jesus ministered comfort throughout his earthly ministry, often identifying with the hurt of others to the degree that he wept with them (John 11:35, Luke 19:41). Even on the eve of his death, he comforted his disciples as he sensed their sorrow and anxiety (John 14:1, 18; 16:33).

We can be assured that God will comfort us in our distress because he has said that he is the "God of all comfort who comforts us in all our troubles" (2 Corinthians 1:3). The Holy Spirit is often referred to as the "Comforter" (John 14:16, 26; 15:26, 16:7). The Greek word for comfort (and the word used to describe the Holy Spirit's ministry to us) is "parakaleo" which means "to come to one's side, to one's aid" and suggests the ability to console and give aid.

How can we minister comfort to other people? (Also, refer to chapter four.)

1. Be sensitive to recognize when people need comfort and be available and willing to minister to them.
2. When someone needs comforting, refrain from reasoning ("The reason this happened was..."), teaching, ("Next time..."), or giving advice ("If I were you, I would..."). Instead, learn to *empathize* with those who are hurting. Comfort is an emotional response to another person's emotional pain. The need for comfort cannot be met by rational responses such as correction, teaching, or giving advice.
3. Learn the "vocabulary of comfort" – phrases like, "I'm so sorry that you're hurting." "I hurt for you." "I love you and I want to pray for you right now." "I'm on your side and I'm committed to help you through this." These phrases can be communicated verbally or in writing.
4. In addition to verbal expressions of empathy, use appropriate physical gestures to administer comfort. If done sensitively and sincerely, a warm embrace, holding hands, or wiping a fevered brow can bring comfort.

7. I feel *encouraged*.

The need for encouragement can be met by urging other people to persist and persevere toward a goal and by stimulating them toward love and good deeds.

> "Therefore encourage one another and build each other up" (1 Thessalonians 5:11).
> "And let us consider how we may spur one another on toward love and good deeds" (Hebrews 10:24).

God meets our need for encouragement by providing us an abundant life through Jesus (John 10:10) and by promising us that he will never leave or forsake us (Hebrews 13:5). During his earthly ministry Jesus continually encouraged his disciples and those who were downcast and discouraged. The Pharisees even criticized Jesus because he regularly met with those who were spiritually and emotionally struggling (Matthew 9:12-13). God continually encourages us through the ministry of his word, the presence of his Spirit, and answered prayer.

How can we minister encouragement to other people?

1. Encourage others to set goals and then help them to achieve them. Encourage your spouse, children and friends to live productive lives by helping them develop God-given plans and goals and then become actively involved in helping them reach those goals. If they're already goal-oriented, learn what their goals are and help them to succeed.
2. Recognize when others are discouraged and minister encouragement to them. We all have times of discouragement (we can even become "weary in well-doing"), and when we do, we need to be encouraged.
3. Encouragement can be administered through a phone call, card or letter, or personal visit. Make it a habit to perform several encouraging gestures each day.
4. Let people know you're praying for them. If people perceive that you are a person of prayer, they'll be encouraged to know that you're praying for them.
5. When someone is discouraged, treat him to dinner at his favorite restaurant, invite him to see a movie, or spend a long weekend together; often, just a change of routine is encouraging.

8. I feel *respected*.

The need for respect is met by valuing, honoring, and regarding other people and by treating them as important.

"Honor one another above yourselves" (Romans 12:10b).
"Show proper respect to everyone" (1 Peter 2:17).

During his earthly ministry, Jesus ignored all the social prejudices of his society by showing respect to tax collectors, Samaritans, the poor, lepers, and women. He treated all people as equals.

God considered us to be of such great worth that he sacrificed his only Son that we might be redeemed. Furthermore, he respects our individuality and the sovereignty of our wills in that he will not force himself or his will upon us, but he allows each person to decide for himself whether or not he will receive what God has to offer.

How can we respect other people?

1. Before making any commitment that impacts another person's life, take time to discuss it with him fully. For instance, marriage partners should discuss business commitments, trips, houseguests, major financial outlays, and other decisions *before* commitments are made. Parents should discuss with each other (and even with older children) issues such as household chores and rules of discipline.
2. Solicit and show deference to other people's opinions. Everyone is entitled to his or her opinion regardless of gender or age. Because opinions are so personal, the need for respect is satisfied when we ask people to share their opinions and particularly when we show deference to their opinions.
3. Respect other people's property, privacy, and personal preferences. Take proper

care of objects that you borrow, property you're on, and places you're in. When you're visiting someone's home or office, show proper respect for his property. Honor other people's right for privacy. Knock before you enter your child's room. If your spouse wants solitude, honor her request. If your spouse wants the bathroom towels folded a certain way, honor his preference.

4. Respect other people's time. Always be prompt for appointments; being late indicates a disrespect for other people's time and schedule. In one sense, when we make others wait on us, we're actually robbing them of a valuable commodity: time.

5. Eliminate all prejudices, especially those regarding race, gender, color, and nationality because none of these issues should inhibit our respect for another human being. Any form of cultural bias or favoritism undermines respect.

9. I feel *secure*.

The need for security is met when we establish harmony in relationships and provide freedom from fear or threat of harm.

"Live in harmony with one another" (Romans 12:16a).
"If it is possible, as much as depends on you, live at peace with everyone" (Romans12:18).
"May those who love you be secure" (Psalm 122:6).

During his earthly ministry, Jesus offered security to those who were close to him by continually meeting their physical, relational, and spiritual needs. At times he even performed a miracle to meet a physical need such as the need for food (feeding of the five thousand).

God meets our need for security in that he has promised never to leave or forsake us (Joshua 1:5, Matthew 28:20, Hebrews 13:5). He will always meet our need for food, clothing, and shelter (Matthew 6:25-32); and those who trust Jesus as Savior are eternally secure (John 10:28).

How can we minister security to other people?

1. Seek to increase "relational" security in all relationships. For instance, a husband should live in such a way that his wife does not worry about his faithfulness. Friends should demonstrate a depth of commitment that will prevail through "thick and thin." Children should feel secure in knowing that their parents will always care for and love them, and that divorce will never disrupt the family unit. In a single parent household, the parent can assure the child that the parent will never leave or forsake the child.

2. Provide financial security for those to whom you're responsible. For instance, spouses and parents should provide financial security for their families by having adequate insurance, operating on a budget, adhering to Scriptural principles of finances, having a good work ethic, developing marketable skills, producing adequate income, having a viable will, and maintaining a savings account. Employers can provide financial security for their employees by adapting and adhering to fair employment policies, operating the business on Scriptural principles, caring more for the well-being of people rather than the bottom line, and providing adequate plans for employees' futures.

3. Let people know that you're aware of their physical, emotional, and spiritual needs and that you're committed to being a part of God's provision to meet those needs. We're *satisfied* when our needs are currently being met; we're *secure* when we know that our

needs will be met in the future.

4. Be consistent in how you relate to people. Extreme mood swings will undermine our ability to establish security in a relationship. If we're constantly "up" one day and "down" the next, those close to us will always be wondering, "What's he going to be like today?" On the other hand, emotional consistency develops security.

10. I feel *supported*.

The need for support can be met by coming alongside someone who is struggling or who has a problem and providing appropriate assistance.

"Carry each other's burdens" (Galatians 6:2)

God met our ultimate need for support by anticipating the great burden that we could not bear ourselves (the punishment for our sins), and by committing his personal resources (his Son Jesus) to do whatever it took (he suffered in all ways and was tempted in all ways) to bear our burdens.

During his earthly ministry Jesus invited the multitudes to "Come to me, all you who are weary and burdened, and I will give you rest" (Matthew 11:28). When Jesus completed his earthly ministry, the Holy Spirit was given to us as the Paraclete, the "one called alongside" who will teach (John 14:26), encourage (Acts 9:31), comfort (John 14:16), assure (Romans 8:16), guide (John 16:13), and intercede (Romans 8:26) for us.

How can we minister support to other people?

1. Anticipate and notice when people are experiencing periods of high stress and be available to help them. Stressful times can produce more pressure than one person can bear, in which case the support of others is necessary.
2. Offer to use personal resources to help support others. 1 John 3:17 says, "If anyone has material possessions and sees his brother in need but has no pity on him, how can the love of God be in him?" Using personal resources can not only meet the practical needs of those we're ministering to, but they will also be uniquely encouraged and blessed when they know that we are sharing out of our own resources.
3. Be willing to do practical tasks to help others. Running errands, washing dishes, baby-sitting, yard-work, house-sitting, or house cleaning may provide just the "boost" someone needs.

A fantasy world or a picture of the "abundant life"?

Imagine experiencing life in this way:
- Whenever you experience painful emotions such as hurt, anger, stress, fear and condemnation, you are able to process these emotions immediately so that they do not continue to bother you. Your emotional cup is emptied of painful emotions on a regular basis.
- You are living in such close community with family and friends that they are continually pouring encouragement, approval, attention, etc. into your emotional cup.

Is this a picture of an unreal, imaginary life? Living in an emotional Shangri La? No, this is a description of the emotional well-being that God wants each of us to enjoy. Perhaps it is, in part, what Jesus described when he promised us a full, abundant, and meaningful life (John 10:10).

Group discussion questions (Discuss these issues in your group or with your journeymate.)

1. What was the most interesting concept presented in this chapter?
2. In this chapter we discussed ten emotional needs that we all have. Why is it more effective and satisfying when others take the initiative to *give* to us to meet these needs rather than our having to demand that someone meet them?

Journeymate time

1. Share with your journeymate the results of your homework from last week.
2. While we all basically have the same emotional needs, the *priority* of these needs is different for each person. Review the ten needs listed in this chapter. Choose the three needs that are most important to you: _____, _____, _____. Tell your journeymate about these needs and discuss how each of you could be a part of meeting each other's most important needs.

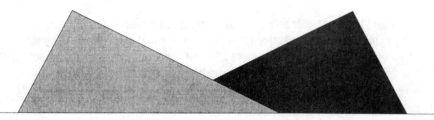

Chapter Summary

1. This last chapter introduces the idea that once we empty our emotional cup of painful emotions, we need to fill it up with positive emotions. The process of emptying our cup of painful emotions and filling it with positive ones is a continual, never-ending process.

2. One approach to engaging in positive emotions is to identify some primary, important emotional needs that we all have and then develop a working knowledge of what they "look like" and how they can practically be given to each other. Using excerpts from the book *Top Ten Relational Needs* (Ferguson, McMinn and Walter), ten emotional needs are discussed.

3. The *Top Ten Relational Needs* book would be a good follow-up study to this workbook.

INTIMATE LIFE MINISTRIES

Intimate Life Ministries (ILM) is a training and resource ministry whose purpose is *to assist in the development of Great Commandment ministries worldwide.* Great Commandment ministries—ministries that help us love God and our neighbors—are ongoing ministries that deepen our intimacy with God and with others in marriage, family, and the church.

Intimate Life Ministries serves
- The *Great Commandment Network of churches and ministries,* seeking to fortify homes and communities with God's love,
- A *network of pastors and other ministry leaders* walking intimately with God and their families and seeking to live vulnerably before their people,
- A team of *accredited community trainers* committed to helping churches establish ongoing Great Commandment ministries,
- A team of *professional associates* from ministry and other professional Christian backgrounds, assisting with research, training, and resource development,
- A team of *Christian broadcasters, publishers, media, and other affiliates,* cooperating to see Great Commandment ministries multiplied,
- Headquarters staff providing strategic planning, coordination, and support.

HOW CAN INTIMATE LIFE MINISTRIES SERVE YOU?

The Great Commandment Network is an effective, ongoing support network for churches, ministries, and Christian leaders. There are at least four ways ILM can serve you:

1. Ministering to ministry leaders
ILM offers a unique two-day *Galatians 6:6* retreat to ministers and their spouses for personal renewal and for reestablishing and affirming ministry and family priorities. The retreat accommodations and meals are provided as a gift to ministry leaders by cosponsoring partners. Thirty to forty retreats are held throughout the U.S. and Europe each year.

2. Partnering with denominations and other ministries
Numerous denominations and ministries have partnered with ILM by "commissioning" them to equip their ministry leaders through the Galatians 6:6 Retreats along with strategic training and experiential resources for ongoing ministry. This unique partnership enables partner organizations to use the expertise of ILM trainers and resources to perpetuate a movement of Great Commandment ministry at the local level. ILM also provides a crisis-support setting where partners may send ministers, couples, or families who are struggling in their relationships.

3. Identifying, training, and equipping lay leaders
ILM is committed to helping churches develop relational leaders through:
- *Sermon series*
- *Experiential, user-friendly resource packages*
- *Weekend Workshops*
- *Great Commandment Living Conferences*

4. Providing crisis care and support
The Center for Relational Care provides support to relationships in crisis through Relational Care Intensives for couples, families, and singles.

For more information:
Intimate Life Ministries
P.O. Box 201808
Austin, Texas 78720-1808
800-881-8008
www.GreatCommandment.net

6Acts Ministry

6Acts Ministries is devoted to:

...*teaching* life-giving truths in an engaging manner
...*developing* leaders who significantly impact their culture
...*producing* resources easy to understand but hard to ignore

Teaching life-giving truths - 6Acts Ministry Offers These Seminars:

11th Commandment Seminar

Based on the popular 11th Commandment Project resources, this seminar will profoundly and positively affect all your relationships. It's a marriage seminar, parenting seminar, singles seminar, work-place seminar—all rolled into one! This life-giving seminar will introduce 35 verbs (the One Anothers of Scripture) that will forever change the way you relate to others.

Emotional Fitness Seminar

"Deal with your emotions or your emotions will deal with you!" That's good advice. This seminar presents a biblical perspective on human emotionality. It teaches practical lessons on how to deal with the major emotions of life: hurt, anger, guilt, fear, condemnation, and stress. You'll learn how to manage your own emotions and how to properly respond to the emotion of others.

Entering His Presence

Jesus declared that the most important thing is life is to love God (Matthew 22:37). This seminar focuses on practical ways to enhance both individual and corporate worship.

Staff Development Retreats

"Come with me by yourselves to a quiet place and get some rest" (Mark 6:31). Often, the most beneficial thing a church or ministry staff can do is to set aside time for personal renewal and refreshment, sharpening ministry skills and getting a fresh vision from God.

Developing leaders through Strong Ties Ministry:

- A fraternity of worship leaders who care for one another.
- A ministry that focuses on worship leaders—not on what you do or the products you use—our ministry is to you.
- A community of worship leaders who are strongly connected and committed to one another.

Strong Ties Ministry offers four services:

- Strong Ties Worship Leaders' Retreat—annual three-day retreats for renewal and equipping.
- Worship Connection—a placement service for churches and worship leaders.
- Strong Ties Web—a relational web that offers encouragement and caring involvement.
- L3 - Life Long Learning - a dynamic program to help ministers develop life skills,

ministry gifts and to engage in continuous learning.

Producing resources - for a complete listing of resources, visit 6Acts.org.

For more information:

6Acts Ministry
2322 Creekside Circle South
Irving, Texas 75063
972.432.8690
www.6Acts.org
dmcminn@6Acts.org